H680

629.13
F   **Floherty, John J**
       Aviation from the ground
          up

Date Due

OCT 15 1969	DEC 2 1971	JAN 28 1974	Oc 17 '79
JAN 20 1970	DEC 22 1971	MAR 28 1974	No 19 '79
APR 9 1970	FEB 3 1972	MAY 16 1974	JAN 12 1981
OCT 28 1970	FEB 17	DEC 6 1974	OCT 19 1981
NOV 11 1970	MAR 3 1972	JAN 23 1975	APR 4
NOV 11 1970	MAR 23 1972	FEB 19 1975	SEP 22
NOV 30 1970	APR 1 1972	OCT 14	
FEB 23 1971	APR 27 1972	OCT 28 1975	MR 28 88
MAY 20 1971	NOV 10 1972	JAN 16 1976	NOV 20 '89
OCT 7 1971	MAY 17 1973	MAY 11 1976	OC 13 93
	NOV 20 1973	NOV 1 1976	AP 13 94

The history of aviation, the training of
aviators, and the construction of aircraft
are traced in this illustrated volume.

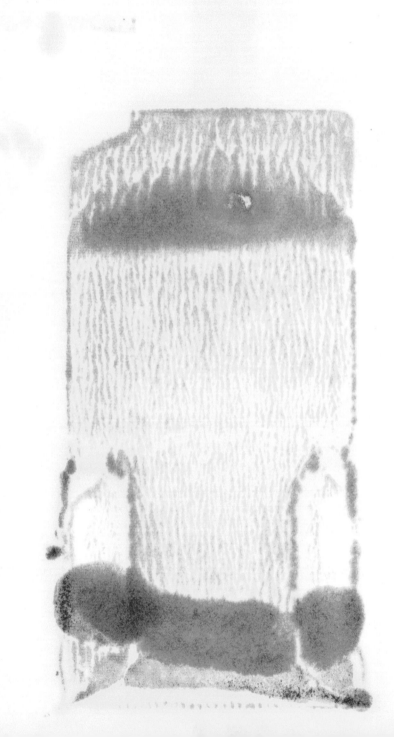

AVIATION FROM THE GROUND UP

Books by John J. Floherty

FOREST RANGER

TROOPERS ALL: STORIES OF STATE POLICE

MEN AGAINST DISTANCE: THE STORY OF
COMMUNICATIONS

DEEP DOWN UNDER

SEARCH AND RESCUE AT SEA

HIGH, WIDE AND DEEP: SCIENCE AND ADVENTURE
WITH THE COAST AND GEODETIC SURVEY

OUR F.B.I.: AN INSIDE STORY

TELEVISION STORY

AVIATION FROM THE GROUND UP

WATCH YOUR STEP

BEHIND THE SILVER SHIELD

WHITE TERROR: ADVENTURES WITH THE ICE PATROL

MEN AGAINST CRIME: THE INSIDE STORY OF T MEN

FLOWING GOLD: THE ROMANCE OF OIL

MONEY-GO-ROUND

With Mike McGrady

WHIRLING WINGS

YOUTH AND THE F.B.I.

SKIN-DIVING ADVENTURES

Aviation
from the Ground Up

By JOHN J. FLOHERTY

WITH 32 ILLUSTRATIONS FROM PHOTOGRAPHS

J. B. LIPPINCOTT COMPANY

PHILADELPHIA AND NEW YORK

To
Johnny-boy
***a** great pal and a fine person*

BY WAY OF INTRODUCTION

This is neither a textbook nor a treatise. It is rather the gleanings of a reporter who has seen aviation grow from a precarious sport to one of the world's most vital industries. It is also the story that has resulted from one of the author's most thrilling assignments.

During the time it has taken to secure the necessary material I have flown with some of the world's best pilots in many types of planes and have observed airmen and airwomen, too, going about their work-a-day tasks in the sky and on the ground.

By special dispensation I was privileged to witness the evolution from drafting table to stratosphere of the jet-propelled defenders of the freedoms we hold sacred. I walked mile on mile of factory floors, observing the miracle of assembling tens of thousands of parts into a whole that would presently throb with power and speed surpassing the dreams of but a decade ago. I wandered through shops where maintenance men worked to keep these jet-propelled planes on the wing. I visited air-school classrooms where the fledglings of today study to be the fliers of tomorrow who will be our guarantee of America's supremacy in the air. I interviewed executives on whose shoulders rested the burden of making progress before profits, and chatted with skilled workers who thank their lucky stars for a high school or college education that has enabled them to take their places in the ranks of the chosen artisans without whom aviation would stop at the drafting table.

In short I tell the story of aviation as I saw it and lived it over a long period of time.

I am deeply indebted to many concerns and individuals in the industry, for the courtesies they extended to me and for the help and advice they gave while I was gathering my material.

My thanks go particularly to American Airlines, Pan American Airways, Colonial Airlines, Douglas Aircraft Company, United Aircraft Corporation (Pratt and Whitney, Standard Hamilton Propeller, Sikorsky Aircraft), Grumman Aircraft Engineering and Aeronautical Academy.

My gratitude goes also to Lauren Lyman, Ted Stern, Lee Warrender, Wayne Davis, Joseph Gaeta and his associate test pilots and to the scores of men in coveralls who bore with me while I asked endless questions.

John J. Floherty

Contents

*The illustrations are grouped,
following pages 32 and 96*

AVIATION FROM THE GROUND UP

CHAPTER ONE

Those were the days

From the vantage point of my studio windows high above picturesque Manhasset Bay I have watched aviation grow from a timid and tottering infant to a winged giant thundering across the skies.

Western Long Island will always be remembered as the cradle of flying in the United States.

Fifteen aviation centers, scarcely more than a minute's jet flight from where this is written, have been the scenes of over a hundred history-making flights. Each flight was a milestone in the development of what was once considered a reckless, neck-breaking sport into one of the world's most vital industries.

Nearby Garden City witnessed in 1909 the flight in which Glenn H. Curtiss won the *Scientific American* Cup when he flew twenty-five miles in fifty-two and a half minutes. The course was around the flying field on which an emergency landing could be made at any moment. More daring was Charles Willard who within a month after Curtiss' record made a cross-country flight of twelve miles from the same field. Before another month had passed Wilbur Wright startled the world by flying from Garden

City around the Statue of Liberty and back, a distance of forty-two miles.

The following year Clifford B. Harmon flew from Garden City to Greenwich, Connecticut, winning the Country Life in America Trophy. While the distance flown was only twenty-one air miles, it included a ten-mile hop over the waters of Long Island Sound, an unheard-of feat in those days.

The following year in a series of contests of speed, altitude and endurance, it was proved to all but the most skeptical that the airplane had come to stay and that human flight was an accomplished fact.

Glenn Curtiss made an exhibition flight at Sheepshead Bay, carrying a gunner from the Army post on Governor's Island. It was the first demonstration of aerial gunnery. Authorized to carry the first air mail, Earle Ovington made a flight from Garden City to the neighboring village of Mineola.

In the same vicinity the United States Army participated in an air meet at which Lieutenant H. H. Arnold flew a Wright biplane. In his memoirs the late General Arnold recalls that in those days an officer participating in an air meet must pay all expenses from his personal funds. At the end of the meet young Arnold was flat broke, without enough money to pay his railroad fare back to New York, to say nothing of his hotel bill. A friend, also financially flat, came to his rescue. Moving among the spectators, he announced barker style that the Army flier had consented to fly passengers for a modest fee. A wealthy sportsman was the first to accept the offer. The young lieutenant and his passenger had been in the air but a few minutes when a sudden rain squall buffeted the little plane. The lieutenant's skill, only lately acquired, plus a dash of good luck enabled him to make a safe landing and to roll the plane under its own power into the primitive hangar. The passenger who had agreed to pay fifty dollars for the ride, handed his pilot a hundred dollar bill. Embarrassed, the young flier said he could not make change. "Never mind," replied the passenger, glad no doubt that he was still alive, "some other time will do." Then he hurried away.

Many years later, when stars had replaced the bar on the young flier's shoulders, Arnold met his passenger of long ago at a social function and gladly returned the fifty dollars' change.

As the months passed, the fledgling "aeroplane," as it was then called, began to try its wings in exploits that became more and more daring. Lincoln Beachey, a noted flier in those days, raced his plane against an automobile, driven on the Sheepshead Bay track by Barney Oldfield, a race driver whose fame had spread over the Western Hemisphere. Then came a flight from Westbury, Long Island, to Gaithersburg, Maryland, a distance of 264 miles in the then-startling time of four hours and fifty-one minutes. The plane had proved how far it could fly. Presently it was to prove how high it could fly when D. L. Thompson reached a height of 14,020 feet with one passenger. During the next two years records were knocked over like bowling pins.

For instance, Captain A. Silvio covered a distance of 330 miles from Norfolk, Virginia, to Mineola, Long Island, with eight passengers, a feat which many believed could never be accomplished. Shortly thereafter the postal authorities began to take notice. It had now become evident that the airplane was fast becoming a practical and rapid means of transportation. In May, 1918, the world's first regular airplane service was inaugurated between Belmont Park, Long Island, and Washington, D.C. Soon the service was extended to Boston and later to Chicago. The Chicago run took thirty-six hours and fifty-six minutes, including an overnight stop at Cleveland. The following year the first passenger air service in the United States was established. A Mrs. Hoagland and a Miss Hodges were the first paying passengers to fly from Long Island to Atlantic City and return in a flying boat piloted by Robert Hewitt.

Meantime the more intrepid of the birdmen were dreaming of conquering the stormy Atlantic. Many of their dreams proved to be nightmares. Undaunted, however, they worked tirelessly for the accomplishment of their life-or-death adventure until one day in May, 1919, three seaplanes, NC-1, -3 and -4 took off from Rockaway, Long Island, and were soon rapidly diminishing specks on the first leg of transatlantic flight. Only the NC-4 completed the flight under its own power.

Not to be outdone, the British sent the dirigible R-34 on the first round-trip transatlantic voyage. I was present when it landed at Roosevelt Field. It was a thrilling sight. A hundred men hung on like grim death to the ground ropes flung down from the giant gas bag. Row on row of sandbags tethered the gargantuan sausage to the ground. The shouts of assembled spectators merely made a background for the exhausts of throttled motors. It was a stirring scene although something of an anticlimax as far as flying the Atlantic was concerned.

That evening while driving from the field with a well-known pilot, I asked, "Will the lighter-than-air craft be a serious competitor of the airplane?"

"Never," he said promptly. "You must remember that the dirigible, no matter how well engineered, is merely a big bubble of inflammable gas that the tiniest spark in the wrong place will destroy. You will hear of that occurring one of these days."

His words were prophetic, for in 1937 the giant dirigible *Hindenburg* exploded at Lakehurst, New Jersey, killing thirty-five passengers and her commanding officer. It was the climax to a series of dirigible tragedies that all but destroyed the lighter-than-air craft industry.

In 1920 four DH4-B planes, commanded by Captain St. Clair Street, flew from Mineola, Long Island, to Nome, Alaska, in fifty-five hours actual flying time. During the same year the passenger-carrying record was shattered. A single-motored plane, a Curtiss Eagle, flew over New York City with nine men and women aboard. The feat was so spectacular, it made the headlines in the press of the world. The ensuing summer a Loening monoplane, known as the *Flying Yacht,* established a new altitude record, 19,500 feet, with four persons aboard.

Since the flight was made over Port Washington, Long Island, my home town, I had a grandstand seat. From a window in my studio I followed its progress upward until at ten thousand feet it became a speck so small that I lost it in the limitless blue. At that time it did not seem possible that man, burdened by a ton, more or less, of dead weight, could soar far higher than an eagle dared venture.

Those were the days when men knew only the bare rudiments of aviation. One by one they flew farther and faster and higher and sustained flight for longer periods. Stinson remained aloft for twenty-six hours of continuous flight over Roosevelt Field. In March, 1923, Macready and Kelly made a nonstop flight from Long Island to San Diego, California, 2,516 miles in twenty-six hours and fifty minutes. Russel Maugham flew approximately the same course between dawn and dusk. Cyrus Bettis won the Pulitzer Trophy race at Mitchell Field in a Curtiss V-1400 when he set the world's record for a hundred kilometers at 249 miles per hour.

At the many flying fields within a short drive from my home I had ample opportunity to observe those pioneers

at close range. Without exception they were zealots to whom the future of civilization hung precariously on man's ability to take to the air. Many a time over coffee at the airfield restaurant I heard them discuss in all seriousness flight projects that at the moment seemed to be fantasies of their collective imaginations. I remember well one budding pilot who years later gained fame as a magazine writer. One day at lunch on the field he held forth on the possibility of "rocket flight." It seems that a few days previously he had attached crude wings and tail assembly to an ordinary Fourth of July toy rocket and launched it in a nearby pasture. He had carefully noted every detail of its behavior from its take-off to its dead-stick landing. There were no condescending looks or words from the three seasoned fliers at the table. Indeed, they listened attentively and soon began a round-table discussion of rocket and jet propulsion that left me bewildered and skeptical.

Nearly a score of eventful years in aviation passed before I heard again of jet propulsion. Still a skeptic, my memory leaped back to the youthful flier who dared explore the future, and to his oil-stained buddies who took his twenty-five-cent rocket experiment as seriously as if it had come out of the laboratory of a great scientist.

In those early days flying attracted men who were young in years or in spirit. Taking a contraption of wood and linen, powered by a temperamental motor, up into the "wild blue yonder" was an adventure generously spiced with danger. They were fatalists all. When one's number was up, there was little to be done but to accept the inevitable gracefully. Even among the youngest of them there was neither recklessness nor bravado. Chances were taken only after they were carefully appraised.

Flying personnel had changed little in 1927 when a rangy young man, who looked younger than his years, skill-

fully landed his Ryan monoplane on the field at Mineola.
"My name is Lindbergh," he said quietly. He had flown
from San Diego, California; his destination Paris, France.
Not far from his plane, *The Spirit of St. Louis,* were
two others also waiting for a propitious moment to take
off on a transatlantic nonstop flight. One was owned by
Clarence Chamberlin, the other was officered by United
States Navy Commander Richard E. Byrd. Fog and rain
and blustering winds kept the planes earthbound for days
while newsmen haunted the hangars. Chamberlin had a
passenger with a weakness for publicity; Byrd was bent
on adding to the laurels he had gained in a North Pole
flight. The silent austere Lindbergh had little copy value
for the reporters, that is, for all but a few, one of whom
was Lauren Lyman, a New York *Times* man who later
was awarded the Pulitzer Prize. Lyman, a top-flight news-
paperman also silent and austere, somehow saw success in
the eyes of the evasive Lindbergh. He sensed the spiritual
urge for achievement hidden under the young flier's an-
tipathy to publicity.

The two, newsman and birdman, became friends. It was
a friendship that has lasted to this day. Unexpectedly
one bleak morning Lindbergh took off and disappeared
over the murky horizon with a handful of sandwiches
and a bottle of water for sustenance. Thirty-three hours
and thirty minutes later the "Lone Eagle," as he was
called, landed on Le Bourget Field, outside Paris, and
became overnight a world hero.

While Lindbergh was not the first to fly the Atlantic
nonstop—Alcock and Brown flew from Newfoundland to
Ireland in 1919—he was the first to take off from United
States soil and make a pin-point landing at his predetermined destination in Europe.

At the moment of Lindbergh's landing in Paris a crisis
in the relations between the French and Americans ex-

isted. The situation was so serious that, according to rumor, our ambassador was virtually in a state of frustration. Then out of the black night sky an American youth glided in to a three-point landing. The French people, quick to recognize a hero, went mad with delight. Where harsh words and sidelong looks had existed shortly before, a turbulent multitude shouted, *"Vive l'Americain!"* The daring feat of a young American flier had forged a bond that has grown stronger with the years.

Within a month Clarence Chamberlin accompanied by his passenger flew the Atlantic from Roosevelt Field to Eisleben and set up a new distance record of 3,911 miles in thirty-three hours and thirty minutes.

Two weeks later Commander Richard E. Byrd with a crew of three took off from the same spot with France as his destination. The French coast, however, was shrouded in such dense fog, he was forced to land on the sea off Ver-sur-Mer.

During the three years, 1927 to 1930, that followed no less than thirteen different milestones were set, each an epoch in aviation. Chamberlin and Williams' fifty-two hours of continuous flight, Lieutenant Dallas' transcontinental record in an amphibian plane, Frank Hawks' non-stop flight from Los Angeles eastward to Roosevelt Field, Elinor Smith's endurance record for women, twenty-six hours, twenty-one minutes, Jimmy Doolittle's historic feat, proving the feasibility of blind flying, Russel Boardman's hop to Istanbul, Turkey, a distance of 5,011 miles, were but a few of them. It must be remembered that all those feats were accomplished in so-called "crates" that the greenest pilot student of today would look on with disdain. And yet casualties were comparatively few.

Those were the days when thousands thronged to fairs and carnivals to witness daredevils risk their necks in such feats as wing walking and acrobatic stunts that caused the spectators' hair to stand on end. Lincoln Beachey had demonstrated that a plane could be made to turn somersaults in the air. He called it "looping the loop," a phrase borrowed from a Coney Island bloodcurdling attraction. Those daring fliers, sometimes called "barnstormers," contributed much to the future of aviation. Traveling from state to state and from county to county, they demonstrated to millions of Americans who never before had seen a plane that mechanical flight was a reality. Many a skeptic on witnessing a "flying circus" said with a shake of his head, "If I hadn't seen it, I wouldn't believe it!"

As exhibition flying became a business, the airplane became a source of income for scores of fliers. With only the most rudimentary knowledge of navigation or meteorology few of them could qualify as pilots. When flying to distant points, they followed railroads and highways, occasionally getting lost with disastrous results. It is a curious fact that this terrestrial navigation by rail and road is still used occasionally by our highest-ranking pilots.

By 1933, aviation had conquered long distance. It was in that year that Wiley Post took off from Floyd Bennett Field on his historic solo flight around the world and landed at the same spot just seven days and eighteen hours later. Records, however, were made to be broken. Five years later, almost to a day and from the same field, Howard Hughes circled the globe in three days and nineteen hours.

Flying the Atlantic had now become almost routine. Improved design and construction of planes and engines, the development of more efficient fuels and the use of numerous instruments and devices, all contributed enormously to the safety and performance of aircraft.

As if to prove that it was the man and not the improved machine that made transoceanic flights possible, a mechanic's helper, a young fellow still in his twenties, startled the world while it was still marveling over Hughes' flight in his super-plane.

One morning at the same Floyd Bennett Field, Douglas Corrigan rolled out his nine-year-old Curtiss Robin, much the worse for wear, and with a wave of his hand and an Irish grin on his face took off supposedly for Los Angeles. The few who witnessed his departure were surprised to see him take an easterly instead of a westerly course. Soon the young flier was swallowed in the morning mist over the Atlantic and promptly forgotten.

Next day workers at the flying field were stunned to learn that the lad in the rickety Robin had landed safely at Baldonnel Airfield near Dublin, Ireland. Then and there he was dubbed "Wrong-Way Corrigan" and as such his fame flashed around the world.

And so a legion of pioneers continued to explore in laboratory, shop and sky the myriad mysteries of flight. The feats of which I have told are but a few of the achievements of the earlier birdmen. I have chosen them because they and scores of others had selected my immediate neighborhood as their base or scene of operations. Some of them I watched spellbound from my desk. In fact, over the years the drone of flying motors and the whiplash of props have become as familiar to me and my family as the wail of the wind in the oaks that shadow our home.

In short, I have not only seen but I have heard aviation grow. I remember well the early planes with their spluttering little motors delivering a questionable ninety or a hundred horsepower; they sounded no more formidable than a Model T Ford. But since sunrise this June morning several sky-giants have roared over my rooftree—a Boeing 707 Jet, Europe bound, at five hundred and eighty-five miles an hour, with its four Pratt and Whitney JT3C-6 engines, its wing spread almost the length of a city block, its weight more than a hundred tons. Within its sleek body over a hundred persons enjoyed the ease and luxury of a first-class hotel.

Scarcely had the cyclonic roar of the big Boeing faded in the east when out of the west came the distant rumble of another leviathan, slightly smaller and following the same course. It was a Lockheed Constellation, bound for the Eastern Hemisphere.

In quick succession came a DC-7, a DC-6 and others unidentifiable in the growing overcast, all winging toward various destinations. In the darkness of evening the blinking lights of homing planes passed at intervals as they approached nearby LaGuardia Field and the International Airport, locally known as Idlewild. From those two great air travel centers hundreds of planes fan out day and night over a complex network of airways embracing the world.

Indeed, in June, 1943, a regular commercial around-the-world air service was inaugurated when a Pan American Clipper, a four-engined Lockheed Constellation, took off from LaGuardia Field for Europe with twenty-one passengers. It happened on the afternoon of June seventeenth. That same evening at six-fifty the Clipper landed at Gander, Newfoundland, and arrived in London the following day. The next forenoon it swept majestically into Istanbul, Turkey. In less than twenty hours it came to a stop at Karachi, India, then on to Calcutta, arriving a day later. Next stop was Manila from where it hopped to Nanking and Shanghai. Then to Tokyo and from there to Honolulu with the next stop San Francisco. On June 30, at 5:05 p.m., the world-encircling Clipper rolled along a runway at La Guardia and came to a stop after its scheduled journey of 22,219 miles in 101 hours and thirty-two minutes' flying time.

Now that epochal flight was neither a stunt nor a demonstration; it was merely the opening of a transportation service that is now well established between the far-flung cities on its original schedule.

A stone's throw from my house is the home of a Pan American flight engineer. One day nine years ago I met him as he arrived from LaGuardia Field where he had just left his plane. "Where have you been, Frank?" I inquired.

"Just got in from Calcutta," he replied with as little concern as if he had come from Brooklyn. Transworld travel had become as commonplace as that.

Even then we were getting a glimpse of today's air travel, when cruising speeds of three hundred miles an hour are comparable to the slow pace of the horse and buggy, and when the roar following jet-propelled military fighters, hurtling at seven hundred and fifty miles an hour to and from bases, envelops the community in which I live.

In interviews with leaders in the field of aviation I am always aware of that same spirit of prophecy as marked the early fliers. Engineers, designers, pilots and airline executives are alike in this: all of them men whose thoughts are in the clouds but whose feet are solidly on the earth. When these men speak of the future of air transport, they speak from experience. Many of them have grown up with aviation and have seen it develop from a shoestring enterprise into one of the world's mightiest and most indispensable industries. Their prophecies of some eight years ago: speeds of a thousand miles an hour, rocket propulsion, atomic power, and planes built to carry several hundred persons, do not sound so visionary now that, for instance, Pratt and Whitney Aircraft, under federal auspices, is doing research and development work on a nuclear-powered engine.

As a spokesman for Hamilton Standard Division, United

Aircraft Corporation, said to me the other day: "With some of our products in use already on guided missiles, we are even in the position of taking a science-fiction look into the future and envisaging ourselves providing the air-conditioning system for the first rocket to the moon!" This is more than speculation, for in a government program, Pratt and Whitney Aircraft is building a fuel cell, which converts chemicals directly into electricity, to provide on-board electrical power for the Apollo spacecraft missions leading to manned exploration of the moon.

This same company also developed the first liquid hydrogen rocket engine, the RL-10, a powerplant for the Saturn and Centaur space vehicles.

CHAPTER TWO

Aircraft and crews

The passenger who sat beside me on the DC-7 a number of years ago was an elderly man. His snow-white hair and kindly manner suggested a professor homebound for the Christmas holidays. He sat entranced as he viewed the snow-covered countryside fifteen thousand feet below us. "Beautiful, perfectly beautiful," he murmured occasionally and then lapsed into rapt silence.

Suddenly he turned to me as if we were old friends. "I still marvel at the miracle of flight," he said. "Two days ago I was in Egypt and here we are outstripping the sun across the United States." And so began a long and pleasant conversation, in which I discovered that he was an archeologist.

Presently I noticed that each time the door to the pilot's compartment opened, as one of the crew entered or left, he seemed filled with a boy's curiosity. He craned to catch a glimpse of the hidden zone beyond the bulkhead that separates pilots from passengers. Then it occurred to me that I and, indeed, others among our fellow travelers, were filled with the same inquisitiveness. A woman seated behind us said to her companion, "How in the world can anyone watch so many dials and gadgets! I suppose they are all necessary or they wouldn't be there." My companion, overhearing the remark, turned to me. "That has occurred to me, too," he said in a very audible whisper.

We were now flying through heavy clouds that at times almost obscured the wing tips and at other times thinned out until they resembled steam rolling from a boiling cauldron. The dense vapor, shutting out the sunshine, created a gray twilight. Although sunset was several hours away, the lights in the plane were turned on. The engines, generating thirteen thousand horsepower, purred gently. After a prolonged silence I discovered that my partner was sleeping peacefully.

Tired of reading, I sat gazing out into the infinite void. Below, cottony clouds lay like a soft white blanket over the earth. We were again in sparkling sunlight. The weather report from the ground was "overcast with occasional rain."

Relaxed and comfortable, my thoughts reverted again and again to the rites and rituals that went on hour after hour inside the narrow door in the bulkhead. I was filled with curiosity as to what qualifications were necessary before men were entrusted with half a hundred human lives, to say nothing of the million-dollar investment the plane represented. What were their backgrounds? How and where did they get their training? What were their various functions and duties during flight? Where and how did they secure rest during long flights to relieve them from the nervous strain their jobs entailed? Their pay, their hours of work, their home life and scores of other questions I wanted to ask, crowded through my mind and spurred my reporter's instinct.

Although an old hand in air travel, I marveled, as I had many times before, at the phenomenon of modern air transport. Here were fifty of us, men and women and two small children, hurtling across a continent at better than 365 miles an hour. Fifty tons of dead weight defying gravity. Nearly three miles above the earth in a rarified region where the amount of oxygen present was insufficient to support life, we read or chatted or catnapped or moved about in the most complete comfort. The air in our pressurized cabin was fresh and clean as a sea breeze; the temperature a normal seventy degrees although it was twenty below zero outside the plane. The meal served us was not only of appetizing quality but it was piping hot as if it had just come from the kitchen of a well-ordered home. Now and then soft music floated in from nowhere. Quiet laughter came from the forward part of the cabin; the chatter of a two-year-old from the seat behind me.

An occasional glance through the window made the mystery of it all still more inscrutable. In spite of our speed of six miles a minute the plane seemed to be as motionless as the mountains hidden in the haze below. Only the soft thrumming of the engines and the reflected halos on the spinning "props" destroyed the illusion that we were hanging in mid-air.

My thoughts were interrupted when my friend, the archeologist, awoke with a start. "Dear me," he said apologetically, "I must have dozed off." "Yes," I replied, "it was a nice three-hundred-and-sixty-five-mile nap." He had been asleep just one hour.

"Oh, that's a mere catnap," he answered with a grin. "Last year while flying in a Pan American plane from London to New York, I slept eight solid hours. That was in a sense a remarkable trip. I crossed three thousand miles of ocean and never caught even a glimpse of it until we lost altitude as we approached New York."

During the talk that followed we discussed many subjects, ranging from air travel to inadequate housing. At last he said abruptly, "By the way, where do you live?"

"My home has been in Port Washington, Long Island, for many years," I replied.

"Port Washington," he mused. "Come to think of it, while flying from London I learned that the flight engineer on the plane lives in that town. Nyilas is his name, Frank Nyilas. Perhaps you know him."

"Indeed I know him," I said. "He's a neighbor of mine."

"Small world, isn't it?" the archeologist remarked drowsily and before long he dozed off again.

Weeks had elapsed since I bade good-by to my friend the archeologist. Meanwhile I had chatted with Flight Engineer Nyilas on several occasions. One evening as we sat by the fireplace in my home I am afraid that my role of host was usurped by that of the reporter. My unappeased curiosity about the forbidden area popularly known as the cockpit was overwhelming. "Tell me, Frank," I said, "how many in a crew are required to fly, say, a Constellation?"

"That depends," he said, "on the number of flight hours and the conditions of the flight. When flying without passengers from New York to the Pan American maintenance base at Miami, only a basic crew is required, the pilot, co-pilot and flight engineer.

"In longer flights, to Calcutta for instance, we may have as many as nine people in the crew, the captain, first officer, second officer, third officer, flight engineer, assistant flight engineer, navigator, purser and hostess. The actual flight time is the period between take-off and landing.

"In a flight to San Francisco let's suppose the flight time is ten hours and twenty minutes. The actual time probably would be two hours more because of stops, taxiing to take-off position and unforeseen causes of delay.

"Two pilots must be at the controls at all times. The captain takes over the controls during the take-off and landing. Watches are usually two hours on duty followed by one hour off duty."

"What are the duties of the captain of a passenger plane?" I inquired.

"Like the captain of a seagoing craft, his authority is absolute, particularly when the plane is in flight. He alone is held responsible for the safety of the plane, the passengers, the cargo and the personnel. A change of course may be ordered only by him. The same holds true in unscheduled landings. In an emergency, only he may decide the course of action. Besides doing a formidable amount of paperwork both in flight and on the ground, he acts as a kind of good-will ambassador among the passengers. Much of his off-duty time is spent in study of new devices, new techniques, new rules and regulations. In spite of his thousands of hours in the air there is always something new to learn.

"Every airport presents different problems, the solutions for which he must have at his finger tips. His physical condition is checked by periodical medical examinations. He may not use alcoholic beverages during the twenty-four-hour period preceding a flight. Some companies go so far as to excuse him from duty if and when he is emotionally disturbed through domestic difficulties or for other reasons. His mental fitness is kept at par by periodic instruction which is checked by a series of rigid examinations. His greatest asset, however, is a level head or in other words a goodly store of common sense. No matter how profound his knowledge of flying may be or how proficient his administrative duties, a grain of good sound common sense is worth a ton of book learning when a situation arises for which there is no precedent.

"Safety is his first concern," Nyilas continued. "In the

Operations Manual which governs his every act, a line is printed: NO PRECAUTION WHICH AUGMENTS SAFETY WILL BE REGARDED AS EXCESSIVE.

"Before each flight the captain studies critically the recent and current weather reports and the weather forecast for the route. He also discusses with the operations manager, to whom he is responsible, the recommended flight plan. Then he checks the recent history of the plane, its mechanical condition, fuel consumption and flight characteristics. He checks the gross weight of the plane, the center of gravity location, the stowage and security of the cargo, the quantity of fuel and oil aboard and the condition of the radio equipment.

"When in flight, he prescribes the speed, track and altitude. He checks frequently the work of the navigating officer and sees to it that the plane's radio is manned without interruption. He personally enters in the plane's log any damage to the aircraft, illness and injuries of passengers and crew, abnormal weather conditions, births or deaths or other occurrences outside normal routine.

"The captain is responsible for mail and valuables as well as for the comfort and morale of the passengers. Besides this partial list of the captain's duties and responsibilities, he must set an example for his crew by his gentlemanly conduct, neatness, alertness, firmness and discipline.

"Like the captain, each of his officers has prescribed duties and responsibilities, all of which have to do with the safe and efficient operation of the plane, and actually complement those of the captain."

"And what of the co-pilots, or first, second and third officers as you call them?" I asked. "What are their duties and responsibilities?"

"You must remember that the co-pilot of today is the captain of tomorrow. There is no short cut to the post of command. Long experience as a co-pilot is obligatory. With everything working in good order and the weather fine it takes no extraordinary skill to *fly* a plane. To pilot it, is another matter. To take off, to land, to reach safely a destination in zero visibility, to fight wind and rain and sleet and ice and to cope with the cussedness of things mechanical, to watch a complexity of quivering instruments, switches and controls while scanning the skies and the course over which he is hurtling at three hundred or more miles an hour, all these duties call for a man of unusual capability.

"Such proficiency can be attained by the co-pilot only through endless study, instruction on the ground and during flight. The more he flies, the more he has to learn. Aviation advances so rapidly that the most modern plane becomes more or less obsolescent just about when he has mastered it.

"The first officer is second in command, alternating with the captain as the senior officer on watch. In the absence or incapacity of the captain he automatically assumes complete command. He is responsible for the management of the crew and for the handling and documentation of the aircraft and its cargo at all ports. He must see to it that when the plane is loaded, the center of gravity is at a prescribed position and that the cargo is secured against shifting.

"When he has made a final inspection of the plane and cargo and checked all air controls and needed documents, he makes a search for stowaways. Then having secured an OK from each responsible flight officer, he reports to the captain that the plane is ready for flight.

"The second officer is responsible to the captain for the navigation of the plane and for the care of all navigation equipment. Before each flight he must check all his navigation instruments and see that each is in perfect order.

Physiological training at the Air Force Academy includes a "flight" in an altitude chamber during which cadets are taken to a pressure altitude of 35,000 feet. Here a cadet has had his oxygen supply cut off while working a test problem. This is done to illustrate what would happen should this occur in actual high-altitude flight. The resulting slowdown or stoppage of normal activity is known as hypoxia.

Joseph Gaeta, jet test pilot, one of the heroic group who test
the Grumman Cougars in actual flight. Headphones are concealed in the heavily padded helmet, and the oxygen mask
on the left shoulder contains the receiver. On the left thigh
may be seen the connector tube through which the G-suit is
inflated when pulling out of a dive. On the writing pad
strapped over the right knee the pilot reports the flight characteristics of the plane.

This is the space suit, or MC-2 full-pressure suit, which was worn in the manned aero-space craft, the X-15, by the first man into outer space. This is lighter and offers more protection from extreme heat, cold, etc., than any previous suit worn by an airman.

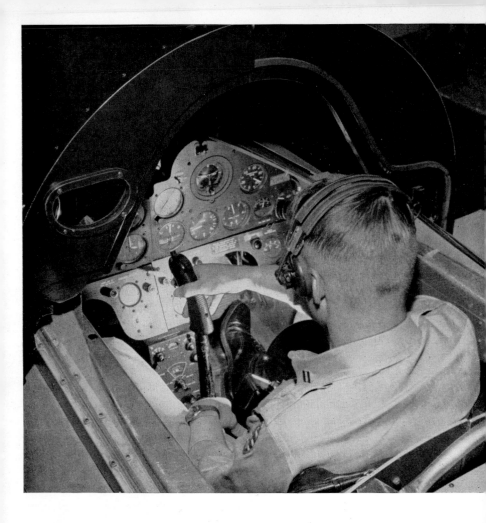

During his four weeks on receiving-instrument instruction, the pilot is introduced to the Jet Link Trainer at Ryndall Air Force Base, Florida. A control panel, operated by the pilot-instructor, can simulate any type of flying condition. The trainer is equipped with sound similar to that of a jet. When flying a weather problem thunder and lightning are simulated. While undergoing this training the pilot receives many hours flying "under the hood"—using only his instruments with the canopy blacked out. At the end of the short four-week course he graduates as a well-versed weather pilot, and ready for instruction on flying radar-equipped fighters.

The U. S. Air Force X-15 rocket ship was shown to the public for the first time on October 15, 1958. Built by North American Aviation for man's first piloted penetration of the fringes of space, the high-speed, high-altitude vehicle was developed under the joint auspices of the U. S. Air Force, U. S. Navy, and the National Aeronautics and Space Administration.

The flight engineer's "desk" aboard a Stratocruiser. There in plain sight are 165 switches, controls, gauges and other devices, each of which plays a vital role in the mechanical operation of the plane.

In the war against pests several thousand planes, similar to the one shown above, are used in spraying crops, swamps and grasslands. From the twenty-two nozzles on the underside of the wing are forced dense clouds of insecticide or weed killer.

A typical airline pilot broadcasts a flight report to his passengers aboard a DC-7.

One of the most famous commercial helicopters, the Sikorsky S-58, carries eighteen passengers besides a crew of two.

A bird's-eye view of the 340th Bombardment Wing ramp at Whiteman A.F.B., Missouri, as the huge B-47 jet bombers were refueled, armed and taxied into take-off position, was made from the wings control tower July 15, 1958, as a world crisis arose in the Middle East.

Templehof Airdrome, one of the key points in the historic Berlin Airlift. With heavily loaded planes landing and taking off at three-minute intervals during the day and night, its runways and taxiing strips were often as congested as highways on a fine Sunday afternoon.

A Douglas giant C-133 turboprop cargo plane, called the Cargomaster, setting new standards of performance as a global carrier. It has a span of 179 feet, 8 inches. Its fuselage is 148 feet, 2 inches long and 16 feet, 2 inches in diameter. The tip of the tail towers more than 48 feet, about the height of a 4-story building. Gross weight of this monster is 255,000 pounds, and it can carry payloads equivalent to twice the normal cargo capacity of the C-124, the largest transport preceding it.

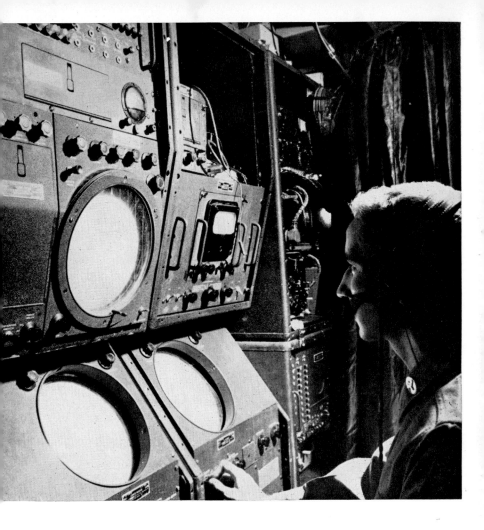

Ground Control Approach, known as GCA, enables the Tower to bring an approaching plane into a safe landing during periods of zero visibility. Through the miracle of radar the operator can see the plane as a pip of light on the three scopes before him and so advise the blinded pilot by radio of his altitude and direction until ground contact has been made.

American Airlines 707 Jet Flagship, powered by four Pratt and Whitney J-57 turbine-jet engines. This Boeing 707 Turbojet is the first jet transcontinental commercial aircraft, and has a cruising speed in excess of 550 miles an hour.

The famous Boeing B-47 bomber.

This is only a partial view of the instruments and controls in the cockpit of the DC-7. Every dial and switch light and lever must be as familiar to the pilot as his A B C. At the lower corners the devices resembling the steering wheel of an automobile are the "sticks" with which pilot or co-pilot directs the course of the plane.

Then he examines critically all the required charts, light lists, navigation and nautical tables and assures himself that they are correct according to the latest available data.

"During flight he is required to take advantage of every opportunity to establish the position of the plane. At a designated time each day he must wind the chronometers and note any deviation. Without accurate time, accurate navigation is impossible. So important is the clock-winding rite that the second officer reports to the captain each time it is performed. He must also enter daily in the log a detailed record of his navigation procedures.

"At the direction of the captain the third officer assists or relieves the other officers in the performance of their duties. Besides helping in preparing the weight and balance manifest, he also supervises the actual loading of the plane in preparation for the first officer's final inspection."

Here I interrupted. "While we, the public, hear a lot about pilots, co-pilots, hostesses and other members of the crew, we seldom hear of the flight engineer. Is there a reason for it?"

"Yes," he said, "the engineer officer was at one time a newcomer in the crew. In the early days of air travel the pilot was the jack-of-all-trades for not only did he fly the plane but he acted as engineer, navigator and radioman. Also he assisted in loading, unloading and often did actual maintenance work. In those days planes were simple, traffic was light, speeds were slow according to today's standards, transoceanic travel had not begun, the stratosphere was still unexplored. In cross-country flying those early transports were rarely more than ten minutes' flying time from a field in which a landing could be made in comparative safety.

"As passenger and cargo traffic grew, planes increased not only in number but in size. With size came mechanical complexities and engineering techniques that were but hazy dreams less than a generation ago. The Boeing Stratocruiser 377 is an excellent example of advances that have been made in aircraft design. With a wing span of over 141 feet, a length of over 110 and a height of over thirty-eight feet, it weighs when loaded 145,800 pounds or over seventy-two tons. It carries 8,000 gallons or twenty-three and more tons of fuel.

"To drive this giant at maximum speed of say 375 miles per hour requires fourteen thousand horsepower in its four Wasp Major engines. To attain even its lower cruising speed of about 285 miles an hour, it must climb some twenty-five thousand feet up into the stratosphere and that demands a pressurized cabin if its occupants are to breathe. Pressurizing calls for powerful air compressions while superchargers are required to supply great gulps of air to the engines, for they too must have their oxygen.

"In the control cabin is a bewildering array of instruments, dials, switches, controls and flashing signals that occupy every instant of the pilot's attention. So you can see how impossible it would be for a pilot to supervise the operation of the mechanical department, particularly of one of the larger planes. Indeed it would be as if the captain of a great ocean liner were to take over the operation of the engine room in addition to his duties on the bridge. That is why you will find a flight engineer on all major transport planes."

"What are the duties of the engineer officer?" I asked.

His eyes sparkled. Pride in his job was reflected in the smile that spread across his regular features. It was as if I had asked a poet to recite his favorite ballad. "Outside of being responsible for the mechanical condition and operation of the plane," he said, "the flight engineer's greatest concern is fuel. You must remember that the best-built, best-officered aircraft is only an inert mass of metal without the fuel that gives it the power to fly."

"With fuel always available at an airport, what might cause a shortage while in flight?" I inquired.

"Several conditions," he said. "Usually strong headwinds or long deviations from the home port due to heavy fog or other unfavorable landing conditions. Pump failure, too, has been known to give an engineer gray hair. He counts the gallons burned as a miser counts his pennies. To him falls the responsibility of loading and personally measuring the plane's supply of fuel and oil before take-off. During a flight he reports at certain intervals to the captain the current content of the fuel tanks.

"Prior to departure on a flight, the flight engineer must make a personal inspection of the plane. This involves a close scrutiny of more than a hundred devices, parts or mechanisms, and then acquaint himself with the history of the plane since his last service aboard it. This he does by reference to maintenance records and previous logs. Should he consider the plane mechanically unfit for flight, he may order defects remedied before the plane takes to the air."

"How are engineering officers chosen and assigned to such responsible jobs?"

"Well, take my own case," he answered. "Although I had a degree in engineering, I started as a grease monkey and for two long years worked in maintenance until I knew by heart every nut, bolt, rivet and screw, to say nothing of engines, superchargers, pumps, electric motors and the hundreds of odds and ends that make a plane tick.

"During those greasy years there were long hours of study. For instance, a DC-7 or any of the larger planes carries a variety of liquids and gases, the properties, uses and storage of wh:ch the flight engineer must have at his finger tips. Take gasoline as an example. Unlike an automobile, a transport plane carries its fuel in as many as nine tanks, most of which are in the wings. A load of fuel may weigh from ten to twenty or more tons. Now that weight must be kept in continuous relation to the plane's center of gravity. When in flight, that weight diminishes at an alarming rate. In a Stratocruiser a ton and a half of fuel is consumed every hour. To keep the plane in balance, the engineer must draw the fuel from the tanks in a way that will insure the load being evenly distributed at all times.

"Then of course there are lubricating oils, hydraulic fluid, alcohol, water, carbon dioxide and oxygen, each as necessary as fuel and each with its own properties and uses.

"The engines, as everyone knows, are the flight engineer's number one responsibility since they supply directly or indirectly not only the motive power for the aircraft but the numerous mechanisms that enter its safe and efficient operation. While the aircraft engine is in itself one of the most reliable power mechanisms, its fuel consumption calls for constant vigilance. Its appetite varies at different altitudes. That is to say, it takes considerably more fuel to fly two hundred miles at five thousand feet altitude than it does at twenty-five thousand or thirty thousand feet simply because the denser air at the lower altitude gives greater resistance. Then too, fuel consumption changes with the various phases of a flight, taxiing, take-off, climbing to the required altitude and level flight.

"A strong headwind draws heavily on a plane's fuel supply while a similar wind in the direction of flight conserves it. Having battled headwinds for long periods, pilots and engineers alike have had anxious moments as news reached them that their destined airport was closed to traffic as a result of zero visibility. With fuel gauges trembling perilously close to Empty, the prospect of flying several hundred miles to another airport where visibility would permit landing is anything but pleasant."

"Then," I asked, "am I correct in assuming that fuel and its consumption are the engineer officer's chief concern during flight?"

His answer was prompt. "It would be more correct to say that it is his most constant concern. You must remember that a plane is an assembly of hundreds of mechanical devices. In a Constellation, for instance, there are some thirty pumps and more than a score of electric motors and mechanical contrivances, all of which demand continuous attention if they are to function efficiently. The fact that mechanical failure is rare in a plane is due to never-ending inspection on the ground and in the air. I have known cases in which the pre-flight inspection of a plane revealed a part or device that was not considered up to the required standard. The result: cancellation of the flight and the loss of considerable revenue. As far as I know, there is no other industry in which every employee from the president down to the hangar sweeper adheres so rigidly to the required standard of safety."

Now that I had learned something of the duties and responsibilities of the technical members of the crew, I inquired about the purser and the hostess.

"What are the duties of the purser or flight steward?" I questioned.

"They are many and varied," the engineer officer replied. "In fact, he is one of the busiest of the crew. Not only does he cater to the passengers' comfort, he also handles the baggage, mail and express en route. He is responsible to the captain for certain of the plane's papers, including those relating to the clearance of the aircraft and all persons on board. He is responsible for the procurement, storage and service of all food used on the plane, as well as for equipment and supplies necessary for passenger service. It is his duty to see to it that all passenger accommodations are kept attractive in appearance and immaculately clean. He acts as advisor to passengers on hotel accommodations, taxi service, foreign currencies and other details of travel.

"He is required to see that safety belts are fastened and that smoking ceases when so ordered by the senior officer on watch. He sees that such articles as coats, umbrellas, overnight bags and so on, are in the passengers' possession before they leave the plane at their destination. Under the captain's direction he controls available space for sale and handles reservations, requests and cancellations. So you see the purser's idle moments are few."

"And the hostess?" I queried.

"Well," he explained, "besides being a hospitable hostess, she is nurse, waitress, baby sitter and mother confessor. She serves the passengers meals prepared by the purser and is sometimes assisted by him."

"Are meals cooked on the plane?"

"No. Only frozen pre-cooked food is used," he said. "It is heated in what is known as a Maxon Oven which automatically brings the food to a certain temperature. Hot coffee is carried in large Thermos containers. All the food is of the finest quality and comparable with that served in the best hotels and restaurants. The meals are served on individual trays and are prepared in a compact galley. When we strike rough weather, as we sometimes do, the hostess is worth her weight in gold. Her unstudied calmness and reassurance are a perfect sedative for passengers who are unaccustomed to air travel."

"How is it possible to secure young women with such poise and versatility?" I asked.

"It's all a matter of careful selection and endless training," he said. "Of course they are chosen with the utmost care but like pilots, engineers, navigators and other personnel, they receive periodic instruction."

"Are air hostesses also registered nurses?"

"A nursing diploma is no longer required on airlines," he said. "During World War II some companies released a number of their hostesses who were also trained nurses to serve with the Armed Forces and in a civilian capacity. A college or high school diploma is now required of all applicants for the position of hostess."

As our discussion ended, my friend the flight engineer said, "To get a true picture of what occurs in the control cabin during a flight, you should see the crew in action and the actual conditions under which they work, particularly when emergencies occur."

"But surely that is impossible," I protested.

"We'll see," he said with an enigmatic smile. "Since you want to see at first hand the physical appointments and accommodations of transoceanic transports, suppose we drive to LaGuardia Airport tomorrow. There you'll find practically every type of aircraft used in American and transatlantic air transport."

Here was my opportunity to explore the secret recesses to which passengers are admitted only on rare occasions.

Bright and early the following morning we left for La-Guardia Airport, scarcely a dozen miles from our homes. Although I had been over the same route scores of times, never had I seen the waters of Long Island Sound so blue nor the air so clear. Here and there against the azure sky several specks of light shimmered in the morning sun. They were homing planes "stacked" at various altitudes, awaiting their turn to make a landing as directed from the traffic tower. The huge bulk of a Stratocruiser, Europe bound, roared by, nosing its way upward to its cruising altitude. Thousands of wild duck, frightened by the violent uproar, took wing from the waters where they had been feeding and flew to a quieter spot. Although among the swiftest birds in flight, their speed was puny when compared to that of the seventy-ton giant hurtling east-ward.

My previous visits to LaGuardia Airport had been merely those of a person hurrying to catch a plane, as one might hurry through a railroad station to make a train. The bustling one-sided street, lined with mammoth build-ings, had seemed to be but another metropolitan avenue glutted with traffic and scurrying people.

That memorable morning, however, it presented a dif-ferent picture. I scanned the brilliant signs on the fronts of the block-long structures that were the roosting places of the giant transports, also the mammoth shops in which an army of mechanics and technicians maintain them in the pink of condition. On the ramp leading to the en-trance of the administration building was a procession of privately owned automobiles and taxicabs. Over the tu-mult of the traffic rose the grumble of idling engines and the rumble of planes taxiing to the appointed runways, while now and then a defiant roar told of the take-off of a plane freed from its leash.

Isolated, yet a part of the stirring scene, stood the vast grouping of buildings known all over the world as the home of Pan American Airways. While being piloted through what appeared to be endless winding corridors lined with offices, I marveled at the quiet of the place where hundreds of people labored in a multitude of jobs, no two of them alike.

A glass partition on the second floor gave a vista into a cavernous building as large as a football field. On the floor were two sky giants at rest, one a Constellation, the other a Boeing Stratocruiser. To appreciate the vast size of the latter, it must be seen indoors. Rising to a height of nearly forty feet, its great wings spread out broadly, its landing wheels shoulder high to a man, its engine nacelles large as five-ton trucks, its four propellers each more than sixteen feet in diameter, this monster defied the imagination to visualize it streaking through the stratosphere at a speed of nearly seven miles a minute.

In its bulbous belly high above the floor was an open door up to which led a flight of steps. As we ascended, a cheery chatter of voices was interrupted by a photographer's flash bulb. The door led into the lounge, a sizable room, luxuriously furnished in the modern manner. Half a dozen fashionably dressed people were seated on divans or standing by buffet or miniature bar. One, a steward in a white jacket, was serving refreshments. It was a scene such as one might find in an exclusive country club. Only the presence of a photographer revealed that the "guests" were professional models being photographed for advertising or publicity purposes. The lounge, I was informed, was popular with passengers during flight; it relieved the tedium of a long air journey.

From the rear of the lounge a richly carpeted stairway led up to the passenger cabin. As we ascended, my thoughts flew back to my first flight in a Curtiss Flying Boat. One of the very few "flying machines" then in existence, it was a tiny affair of wood and lacquered linen with less power than is in a present-day automobile. If someone had told me then that some day I would walk upstairs from the first floor to the second floor of a plane, I would have considered the prophecy a little on the wacky side.

The passenger cabin on the upper deck reminded me of an empty theater: the dim twilight of indoors, unoccupied seats, the oppressive silence.

Arranged in double rows on each side were seats for some fifty passengers. High-backed, roomy and luxuriously soft, it was apparent that they were designed for the utmost in comfort. At the touch of a lever they inclined backward to a sleeping position.

Further forward were berths for twenty-four passengers.

At first glance this section of the plane resembled the interior of a Pullman sleeping car. A closer examination revealed that they were designed for refreshing sleep. About as wide and as long as the average twin bed, they had an inviting look. The mattresses of foam rubber had a sumptuous resilience. Curtains in harmonizing color gave complete privacy. Forward of the sleeping berths were twin dressing rooms, miniature lounges that could be converted into sleeping quarters.

Since Stratocruisers are used by several air lines, the interior arrangement of the plane is designed and built to suit the requirements of the purchaser. A United Air Lines Stratocruiser has what is known as a six-compartment cabin, arranged as follows: Adjoining the control cabin is a section containing eight seats or four berths. Section number two is devoted to dressing rooms. Compartments three and four, containing passenger seats, are separated by a buffet. In the tail section is a private stateroom. On the lower deck is what they call the Hawaiian Lounge, named for the islands to which it flies.

The lounge in the Stratocruiser is situated between the cargo and baggage compartments, each with a cubical capacity almost equal to that of a railroad boxcar.

There now remained the control cabin, or cockpit, to be visited. Entering through a door in the forward bulkhead on the upper deck, we found ourselves in surroundings that bore not even a slight resemblance to the luxuriously appointed passenger compartments. There were no restful color harmonies, no yielding upholstery, no trace of anything that would suggest physical ease.

It was a work place of metal fashioned into a myriad of mechanisms as mysterious and meaningless to a layman like myself as the cuneiform inscriptions on an ancient Assyrian record.

In a space scarcely as large as a telephone booth was

the navigator's desk, now devoid of its usual array of charts and sextants, protractor and parallel rulers. Immediately overhead, a disk of transparent plastic about as wide as a man's shoulders, permitted the subdued light within the hangar to filter through. It was for the navigator's use in making celestial observations with the aid of his periscopic octant.

In the cockpit proper is a bewildering array of dials, switches, gauges, controls with scores of tiny lights, each with its own significance. At first sight the interior of the cockpit has a somber atmosphere, since all panels and instrument faces are black. The numerals, characters and other devices on them, also the numerous switches and strange gadgets of bright metal give a scintillating effect. In the presence of such an indescribable display of unfamiliar objects, I scarcely knew where to begin to ask questions. As if sensing my predicament, my escort, the flight engineer, said, "To get even a slight understanding of what goes on in a cockpit during flight, you must be present and see how the crew operates." He looked at his watch and continued, "We are just in time to observe a practice flight during which the crew copes with a number of emergencies. Let's go!"

We left the great plane through the passenger exit. Descending three flights of steps on a tall staging, we returned to the warren of corridors and offices. At a remote corner of the labyrinth a door opened into a dark recess. We entered, pushing aside heavy black curtains, and found ourselves in what seemed to be the identical place we had just left, the cockpit of a Boeing Stratocruiser.

We had also stepped from daylight into what was apparently a night scene. The instrument panels were illuminated by a subdued light that seemed to come from nowhere in particular. Despite the somberness, hundreds of tiny reflections sparkled from the row on row of instruments and controls. Outside the broad windshield was a dull gray void, possibly intended to simulate a foggy night.

Five men were in the cockpit when we entered. Two were seated in the pilots' seats. The third, a check captain, was seated nearby on the left side. Behind them on the right side the engineer officer sat at his panel on which was an orderly confusion of dials, switches and controlling devices.

Present also was the instructor, a slender studious-looking young man who seemed engrossed with a curious mechanism on the side of the engineer's desk. This device was to play an important part in the events that followed.

As I was introduced to each member of the crew, I detected a slight tenseness such as one observes in those about to take a stiff examination. Indeed the few quips that were passed and the little fragments of laughter seemed to have a forced quality.

During a period of waiting I learned that I was in a Curtiss-Wright Flight Simulator, a million-dollar device designed and built for Pan American Airways. Its purpose: to train flight crews to react correctly under adverse conditions. Newer instruments, higher speeds, new radio aids to navigation, greater weights and wing loading have made more intensive training of flight personnel obligatory. Until recently, practical training was carried on only in actual aircraft costing a quarter of a million to a million or more dollars.

The cost of operating such planes in training flights mounts rapidly into startling figures. To give each of fifty crews a two-hour training flight and two semiannual flight checks costs about two hundred thousand dollars. The cost of the same training in the Flight Simulator is about one quarter of that amount, a saving to the company of more than one hundred and forty thousand dollars.

"What advantages has Simulator training over training in actual flight?" I asked.

Answers came quickly and emphatically: In the Simulator crew members attain an intimate and thorough knowledge of the location and operation of all cockpit controls and instruments before they step foot in a real aircraft. They also develop correct cockpit habits in a shorter time.

"What is meant by 'correct cockpit habits'?" I asked.

"Instinctively doing the right thing on the right split second," came the reply.

"As new operational techniques are developed, crew members in the Simulator can experiment with them without risk. Fast teamwork is as necessary in the cockpit as on the football field. More hours can be spent in developing crew co-ordination.

"There is a certain risk when an aircraft is being handled by training crews whose proficiency has not yet been determined. Simulator training before crew members operate actual aircraft reduces this risk immeasurably.

"Training under simulated emergency conditions is so thorough that crew responses become automatic, so that when in actual flight in case of emergency, the crew instinctively co-ordinates in doing the right thing at the right instant."

Here the instructor looked at his watch. "Okay!" he said crisply.

The men took the positions they would occupy in actual flight. During the few moments of silence that followed, the tenseness I had noted increased perceptibly. Then began the ritual that opens every passenger flight.

The co-pilot intoned in a strong voice some twenty different checks and cross-checks, on each of which the engineer made his verbal report. The CAA (Civil Aeronautics Administration) demands that members of the operating crew be within audible distance of one another when at their stations. Unlike the practice in military planes, no intercommunicating devices may be used.

Presently at a signal from the captain, each of the four motors was started. The simulated grumbling of fourteen thousand horsepower held in leash while warming, was as realistic as anything I had ever heard. Meantime the hands of pilots and engineer flicked something here, pulled something there or twirled something elsewhere. Tension increased as now and then the engines blasted out a short roar.

Presently from the "tower" came radio allowance to taxi to a designated runway. Pips of light flashed here and there on the crowded panels. Deft hands moved with a surgeon's sureness among the array of switches and controls. The beams from the landing lights stabbed through the murk ahead. The rumble of the engines rose to a thundering growl. The pilot with eyes glued to the instruments handled the steering control with the utmost caution. The engines slowed to a mere purr as we arrived on the runway.

Another anxious wait for clearance. Check and cross-check, question and answer between pilot and engineer. Pilot checks radio with tower; "Coming in loud and clear" is the reply. This is followed by, "Clearance for take-off," to pilot. Hands on pilot's and engineer's panels flick here and there like harpists' in a duet. The engines break into a steady roar. The ground speed indicator soon shows eighty miles an hour.

Here the instructor called out, "Truck on runway!" and so created an "obstruction" that, though imaginary, was as real as the Rock of Gibraltar. Again hands flew with lightning speed. Propellers were reversed, brakes applied and a score of operations were performed in nothing flat. In the subdued light I saw beads of perspiration on the co-pilot's forehead.

The engines were slowed down to the merest rumble while co-pilot, captain and instructor engaged in a short but sharp discussion. Despite the technical jargon I learned that in his quick manipulation, the co-pilot's hand had fumbled one of the controls. Soon it was decided that he should reach for that control with palm up.

The take-off was begun again when clearance had come from the tower. Again the motors roared. I watched the speed indicator climb to more than a hundred miles an hour. Presently we were airborne and climbing to the required altitude. Now the engines were in full voice. Little Maltese crosses of light, no bigger than buttons, blinked on the panels like fireflies. On the left seat the pilot with his eyes fixed on the flying instruments handled the stick with deliberate movement and complete concentration. The stick is the control that steers the plane. It resembles an automobile steering wheel with its upper part cut away. When we had gained the required altitude, twenty thousand feet, the speed of the engines was reduced for level flight.

Now the instructor made an adjustment of the device on the side of the engineer's desk and surreptitiously pushed a button. Instantly a fire gong clattered, a brilliant red light flashed on. "Fire in number one engine!" It was the engineer's voice, a trace of controlled excitement in it. Immediately so many things were done by the crew, I could not keep track of them. Hands flew with amazing rapidity among the controls. Pips of light blinked all over the panels. The nimble fingers of the flight engineer flicked through the maze of switches in obedience to the tiny light warnings. In a calm but urgent voice the captain ordered, "Return to base." The pilot at the stick obeyed. I watched the compass indicate a 180-degree change of direction. Soon the fire was reported "out." The crew could not conceal its relief when the crisis had passed.

Almost before nerves had calmed, certain of the red light sentinels warned of ice forming on the propellers. Again the crew went into perfectly co-ordinated action while sprays of alcohol dissipated the deadly ice.

Soon we were confronted by another emergency! Inside the leading edge of the Stratocruiser's tail is a duct through which heat is forced to prevent the formation of ice. Now the heater was "afire." Here was a crisis, nearly a hundred feet away from the cockpit, yet in a matter of seconds little telltale buttons of light told that all was well again.

As we went through one simulated emergency after another, I became aware of a strange psychological phenomenon. It resembled that curious form of hypnosis that sometimes seizes one when witnessing a powerful stage drama, when fantasy gives way to realism and the audience is moved to laughter or fear or tears notwithstanding the fact that it is all make-believe.

Perhaps it was the incessant roar of the engines and the almost imperceptible vibration from the many mechanisms, or it may have been the tense earnestness of the crew and the uncanny realism of the emergencies that created the illusion of being in the cockpit of a plane in actual flight.

Nor did my hallucinations decrease as the flight continued. I could feel my heart beat faster when the sharp blast of a Klaxon horn announced that the landing gear had failed to work just as we were approaching the imaginary airport. I felt a sense of relief when I heard someone say, "Okay!"

As we glided in and landing lights were turned on, I waited with the usual expectancy for the first touch of wheels to runway and believe me, I was rewarded by hearing the familiar screech as rubber met concrete. When the plane "came to a stop," I had a decided sense of loss of motion and even of the silence that accompanies it.

A bit bewildered, I stepped from the twilight of the cockpit into a sunlit office and there met the executive whose chief responsibility is the unbelievable robot I had just seen in action. Like others to whom I had spoken, he was emphatic as he told of the ultimate need for training crews under conditions in which errors may be corrected and studied without endangering a plane worth more than a million dollars. He recited nearly forty emergency or adverse conditions that require split-second corrective action on the part of the flight crew; and these were but major emergencies; there were scores of minor contingencies, many of which if improperly handled, might well become serious.

The possible emergencies were classified as: landing, fuel pressure, electrical system, the aircraft, propellers and fire. Yet it is interesting to note that major emergencies are so rare as to be negligible. Many of the airlines have completed billions of passenger miles without the occupant of a plane seat suffering as much as a scratched finger.

CHAPTER THREE

Turnpikes in the sky

For several decades after 1903 when Orville Wright made the first power-driven flight of 120 feet in twelve seconds, aviation was concerned solely with the development of the airplane as a means of travel. Year by year distances and altitudes and hours of endurance were increased. Motors developed more horsepower per pound of weight; planes ran the gamut of design, biplanes, triplanes and monoplanes.

In 1909 Louis Blériot flew across the English Channel, a distance of thirty-one miles in thirty-seven minutes, in a flimsy little monoplane made of wood and canvas. It was a prophetic flight. After many emphatic pros and cons as to the merits of the biplane over the monoplane and vice versa, the monoplane survived, as witness the planes used in all branches of today's aviation.

As early as 1910 some bright minds envisaged the plane as a means of transportation of merchandise as well as men. Five bolts of silk weighing sixty pounds were flown from Dayton to Columbus in a Wright biplane. It took nine years, however, to convince businessmen that transportation of goods by air was practicable. In 1919 a rudimentary air express was established but exorbitant rates,

$2.72 per ton mile, soon crippled it. During the succeeding decade all-out efforts were made to establish cargo air routes, but the airlines with their eyes on the growing passenger dollar would have none of it. Besides, neither the speed nor the size of the current aircraft were sufficient for well-established freight transport service.

Then came our entry into World War II. Our kindergarten air service grew overnight to college status. Thousands of lads who in civil life would have held down minor jobs were trained and groomed and briefed into an invincible legion of airmen the like of which the world had never dreamed. The planes that had been adequate in peacetime became obsolete. From the drafting boards of the nation sprang a new breed of aircraft, beside which many of the pre-war transport planes were puny in size, power and speed.

War is a tough taskmaster. Men and material must be transported over long distances with speed and certainty. Oceans became puddle-jumps, far countries became neighboring countries. Planes spread their wings over a world in conflict, bearing loads that were inconceivable in the easygoing days of peace when aviation people reckoned their airloads in pounds rather than tons. By war's end, billions of ton miles of air cargo had become commonplace.

Thousands of skilled airmen, returning from military to civilian life, saw occupational vistas beckoning them into the air cargo field. Surplus war aircraft, at but a small fraction of their original cost, made alluring bait to those who saw in them a practical means of earning a good living, if not indeed a promise of wealth.

Even many of the established airlines had begun to see possible dividends in trucking freight through the skies. In 1944 several of them had begun air cargo operations on a limited scale. By the end of the year they had flown nearly seventeen million ton miles (a ton mile is the equivalent of one ton of freight flown one mile). During the ensuing year the load was increased to more than twenty-two million ton miles.

Here was proof for the men returning from the battle-fronts that their dreams of airborne freight were already realized. Soon air freight lines were crisscrossing the country. Converted war planes, some of them owned and operated by veterans, shuttled from city to city and from state to state, their bellies gorged with every conceivable kind of commodity, including such perishables as cherries, plums, figs, grapes, strawberries, melons, lobsters, oysters and shrimps. To merchants dealing in apparel, the air freight service proved to be unusually profitable because of the rapidity with which fashion merchandise could be carried from the great fashion marts to their stockrooms. They found they could reduce their inventory and by so doing make considerable savings. Instead of the days and often weeks that sometimes elapsed during rail shipments, their merchandise could now be delivered overnight or in a matter of a few hours.

With the advent of the non-scheduled operators the air-trucking business took a sharp rise to fifty million ton miles for all carriers. By 1948 air freight had attained its stride. The scheduled operators were hauling one hundred and forty-three million ton miles while the independent carriers added more than fifty-five million.

An airline executive said to me at that time, "When you consider that air express and air freight ton miles have multiplied forty times in seven years, what they will be within a decade is anybody's guess. One thing is certain, however," he added, "a plane like the Douglas DC-6A, cargo version of the airliner DC-6, is typical of the cargo-carrying plane that will have to comply with the requirement of the great American public."

The decade he spoke of is now more than up. To give some idea of the general status of the air cargo situation today, American Airlines alone carried 94,393,110 freight ton miles and 9,612,993 express ton miles in 1958, as against 37,194,024 freight ton miles and 8,937,664 express ton miles in 1951.

Recently I asked another executive how the public fits into the air freight picture.

"It *is* the picture," he answered quickly. "Without public demand for a thousand and one commodities that are produced in far-off places, we might as well go out of business. In my father's day there was a popular song that went, 'I want what I want when I want it.' That old song title might well take its place with 'E Pluribus Unum' or 'In God We Trust.' It has been the shibboleth of American progress. While other nations debated for months and years and sometimes for centuries over what they wanted, America, young, impatient, virile, shouted, 'Do it now!'

"This American impatience has in a sense been our salvation. People have come to want what they want pronto. That is why we dispatch planes daily from the New York fashion market, loaded with the latest styles, to the Pacific Coast, and likewise planes carrying the Hollywood styles streak through the stratosphere for New York. You see, women's fashion merchandise is a perishable commodity; its value depreciates rapidly once it reaches the retail store. Then such perishables as flowers, fruit, vegetables and sea food demand smooth and swift transport. Orchids are flown to the United States from Honolulu by the tens of thousands; in the late spring luscious Scuppernong grapes, grown in Georgia, reach the epicures' tables in New England even before the local vines are in full bud; fresh sea food is now as available in the Western states as on the seaboard. A broiled lobster, ordered in a Phoenix, Arizona, restaurant, was alive and kicking a few minutes before it was put in the oven, although it had journeyed two thousand miles from Maine where it was taken from the sea the day before."

"How is it possible to keep lobsters alive during such a long journey?" I asked.

The official smiled. "That was the problem that caused us gray hair before we solved it," he said. "Under favorable conditions a lobster can live seven days out of his native habitat, the sea. At first glance it seemed there was no problem in shipping them to any point in the United States. We soon learned differently. We found that the weight surpluses of barrels, ice, seaweed and the hundreds of lobsters that died en route made the freight rates prohibitive. Then we discovered that to survive a long journey, a lobster must be kept moist and at a temperature of fifty degrees. He must have lots of oxygen for his twenty pairs of gills. Furthermore he has a habit of popping his shell at high altitudes and that means his demise. To make matters worse, he is a copious drinker of the fresh water from the melting ice and that too proves fatal. A lobster dead on delivery is about as usable as a last year's Christmas tree. Leakages messed up the airplane so badly, to the detriment of other shipments, that American Airlines barred the temperamental lobster from its planes. In spite of its annoying habits, however, we owe much to it since it spurred us to study shipping techniques hitherto unheard-of. A cardboard container, insulated and waterproofed, was devised. In it the lobster was sealed off from fresh water, pressurized cabins kept him from bursting and the shipping weight was materially reduced. Now that the problem is solved, tens of thousands of pounds of live lobsters are flown daily to scores of inland communities where they are served twelve to twenty-four hours after being taken from the lobster pots of the Atlantic Coast."

"How has your experience with lobsters affected other kinds of air shipments?" I asked.

"Well, let's take again the shipping of fashion merchandise," he replied. "It had been the custom to ship women's dresses and suits in substantial packing cases. Of course that practice not only increased the weight of the shipment but it also necessitated steaming, pressing and shaping each garment before the retail store could present it to the customer, thus delaying its sale and increasing its cost. Then some ingenious person conceived the idea of shipping the garments while they hung on racks. This of course eliminated the expense of packing, pressing and excessive weight, economies which were reflected eventually in the price to the ultimate consumer."

"What are the limitations of air freight?" I inquired.

The official answered promptly, "Chiefly weight and bulk. Broadly speaking, anything that can be loaded in a railroad boxcar can be loaded and carried in a plane. For years a large cargo plane has had a minimum pay load of twenty-five tons. Just as an example: A steamship in the Middle East lay as helpless as a floating log when a rotor in her engine room broke down. The nearest replacement was in New York. Only a few years ago such a vessel would have been laid up perhaps for several months. In response to an order by radio a new rotor, weighing nine thousand pounds, was rushed by plane to Iraq nearly seven thousand miles away. In a few days the vessel was again sailing the high seas.

"Only recently at the Jacksonville Airport I watched the loading of our Eastern Airlines plane. The shipment was lead-sheathed cable consigned for Wisconsin delivery. The cable was wound on huge spools, each weighing eleven hundred pounds. Although I am accustomed to airport activities, I was fascinated by the ease with which those modern loading machines picked up the ponderous spools and laid them gently within the plane."

"What have been some of your unusual cargoes?"

"Well," said the officer, "within recent months we carried from overseas a cargo of elephants. Cargoes of wild animals are becoming commonplace. Of course horses have become seasoned air travelers. Air freight has become popular with the makers of expensive television receivers since it was discovered that the jolts and heavy vibration during rail or truck shipment disturbed delicate adjustments of the instruments. When flood or fire or storm or epidemic strikes remote areas, these speedy cargo carriers are a blessing to stricken communities. Red Cross blood bank and first-aid supplies are streaked across the skies to where they are needed. Serums are kept laboratory-fresh by controlled temperatures during transit. And so it goes. Every day adds new commodities with new problems."

Even as we spoke, a plane heavy with cargo glided in for a landing. The ponderous wheels touched the runway lightly as a fluff of thistledown. When it had taxied to the unloading strip, a tractor-drawn train of dolly cars rolled under the belly of the giant plane. The broad doors of the cargo port were flung open, a chute connected plane with train. Packages, cartons, bundles and boxes in infinite variety began to slide down in an endless stream.

Among the items in the flow of merchandise were a procession of perforated cartons containing thousands of day-old chicks; automobile tires, "cans" of movie film, furniture, leaf tobacco. Scores of unidentifiable packages swept down the chute to be piled neatly with the other merchandise on the train of cars. Even before the plane was completely unloaded, it was difficult to comprehend how such a huge quantity of commodities could be packed into the slender body of the carrier.

Two hundred feet away another cargo plane waited on the broad stretch of concrete while a heavily loaded truck sped toward it from the airport entrance. In a skillful maneuver the driver backed the tailboard of the truck to the side of the plane where the cargo doors stood wide open. Curious as to the urgency of such haste, I sauntered over to the vicinity of the plane. Already three men were feverishly unloading the content of the truck into it. They worked as if their lives depended on their speed. As I drew closer I was surprised to discover that the bundles flung from hands to hands were the latest edition of one of the great metropolitan afternoon newspapers.

I learned later that the papers I had seen shipped were selling on the streets of several cities before the local afternoon papers had come off the presses. Some of the country's leading dailies not only beat the clock by air shipment but maintain planes with which to cover the news. The New York *Daily News* maintains several planes for reportorial purposes, also a flying photographic laboratory. This photographic plane can be seen flying over the locale of all major stories within a radius of two hundred miles of the city, supplementing with aerial photographs all work of the ground cameramen. It is claimed by many that this three-way picture coverage has contributed in large part to the phenomenal circulation of the paper.

The advanced development of the modern plane and the tremendous strides made in the improvement of photographic apparatus have created a new and flourishing industry that may be broadly described as "aerial photography." In the field of topographical survey, for instance, a good plane and camera crew can cover in a single day, when light conditions are favorable, an area that might well take a surveying crew on the ground a whole year to accomplish. Much of the exploration for oil and certain minerals is now conducted from the air.

The possible presence of oil underground is often indicated by contours of the earth's crust that are scarcely discernible to oil hunters on the ground. Searching for these surface indications has proved in the past to be a slow and expensive undertaking. In the oil-rich regions of the Middle East, planes equipped with modern aerial cameras and geological instruments prowl the skies in search of likely oil terrain. Study of the photographs by the geologists and technicians reveals unsuspected contours that seem worthy of immediate ground exploration.

Large fleets of planes now engaged in this type of exploratory survey in many parts of the world, offer splendid opportunities in an exciting and profitable profession to hardy young men who can qualify as skilled pilots, geologists or photographers.

Aerial survey is but one of the numerous functions of the airplane. We know of course that for a number of years aircraft has played a most important role in pest control over farms, forests, communities and resorts. In the age-old war between man and the insect world, man has been the loser. About fifty years ago the area in which I live was sheltered by thousands of magnificent chestnut trees. Today not a single specimen can be found in thousands of square miles on the Eastern seaboard. In the cotton-growing states growers were recently brought to the verge of ruin by the boll weevil. In the corn belt "borers" spread bankruptcy. The invasion of the Japanese beetle was nearly catastrophic in some areas. Millions of people throughout the world have suffered and died as a result of the bites of malarial mosquitoes. As in Biblical days plagues of grasshoppers have left vast areas of fertile land denuded to the brown earth.

Man was impotent before the invading insect armies. To spray or dust by hand was like staying the flow of the tides with a broom. To make matters worse, many species of pests appeared—stowaways in shipments from foreign lands. Bulletins issued by the Department of Agriculture plainly indicated that a crisis of the first magnitude was in the making. Laboratories worked day and night on insecticide formulae that, while lethal to the pests, would prove harmless to humans and wild life. Dispensing them over wide areas quickly and cheaply was another story. It was inevitable when desperate men put their heads together to solve the latter problem, that the airplane would be considered. But here too were disheartening obstacles. The planes of that period were, to say the least, on the temperamental side. No pilot felt entirely safe until he had reached an altitude that in case of engine failure would enable him to glide a considerable distance to a comparatively safe landing spot. Dusting or spraying by plane could be done efficiently only by flying close, very close, to the ground. Mechanical failure under those conditions made the loss of pilot and plane almost certain.

Despite the hazards involved, a few venturesome pilots gambled their lives against the chance of engine failure. Some of them lost, others succeeded, but collectively they proved that the airplane was the answer to a country's prayer for deliverance from the ravaging pests.

Better engineering, superior design, improved instruments, more efficient fuels, more skillful pilots and daring flying techniques soon made the plane as tractable as old Dobbin in harness. A new field of endeavor in the air was opened up, a new industry was born. For the first time the tide of battle changed, with the insects on the losing side.

A resolute army of nearly six thousand planes was engaged in the extermination of pests. In the 1949 campaign against the grasshopper 2,700,000 acres were dusted, and poisoned bran was dropped on tens of thousands of acres in the range land areas.

While the cost of the huge operation was high, it was trivial compared with the losses the plague of "hoppers" would have caused eventually. To defray the expense, farmers paid ten cents an acre, the county fifteen cents, the state twenty-five cents and the Federal Government fifty cents to total one dollar per acre. Agricultural flying might now be considered as "big business."

Besides those engaged in pest control, whole fleets of planes were employed in seeding and fertilizing. The next urgent application of the plane to the solution of the farmers' problems was its use as a weapon of war on weeds. The ammunition it used in its spray guns was a chemical compound known as 2,4-D, short for the sixty-four-dollar word, 2,4-dichlorophenoxyacetic acid. Its action is so powerful, a droplet of it no larger than a flyspeck will stimulate the growth of weed seedlings until they outgrow their roots and die of starvation. Yet it does not harm grasses or most crop plants. Experiments by the Department of Agriculture have indicated that it does not affect humans or animals.

More than eight million pounds of this weed killer are sold annually. From Texas to Saskatchewan, a distance of nearly a thousand miles, is spread a bountiful carpet of fertile land in which wheat and corn thrive and herds of cattle munch nutritious grasses. In this, the nation's larder, aviation is qualifying also for the ranks of big business by increasing the yield of every acre by the wholesale destruction of predatory weeds. Here and there throughout the area are dotted small airfields where the pilots, whose jargon is part agricultural and part aeronautical, are the sprayers and dusters who make war on insects and on weeds.

One of the most successful of the crop-spraying outfits is located at Hays, Kansas, in the heart of two hundred million acres of grain crops and within hopping distance of some five million acres of sage-infested forage land. The presiding genius over the P-T Air Service is a stalwart, dynamic individual, Don Pratt.

Modestly and with a faraway look in his eyes, Don relates the epic of how he marshaled his forces in his war against weeds. Fifty-eight airplanes, twenty-four tractor trucks, thirty-one two-thousand-gallon tank trailers. There are a hundred actual pilots. Ground crewmen, truck drivers and sales agents add another hundred men to his pay roll.

Don in his homespun way looks on the airplane as just another farm implement operated to increase the farmer's yield and consequently his profits.

A test strip of unsprayed land was left on a farm at Colby, Kansas, while 160 acres were sprayed. The unsprayed crop yielded fourteen bushels of weedy wheat per acre. The treated land threshed out thirty-one bushels of clean wheat to the acre. Pratt and his pilots spray nearly two hundred thousand Kansas acres each season at a cost to the farmer of less than the price of two bushels per acre. Pratt's goal is a million sprayed acres.

Sagebrush on grazing land has cost stockmen heavily. By shading the nutritious grass from sunlight, the pesky little shrub impedes its growth, thus depriving grazing cattle of vast quantities of foodstuff that should eventually become beef. A sage-infested tract that barely supports eighty-eight head of cattle will, when cleared of the sage, supply nutrition for 120. Five million acres await Pratt and his rapidly increasing crops of pilots. His daring program has attracted fliers from as far east as Pennsylvania and as far south as Florida.

A Pratt spraying unit consists of three pilots and two

Stearman biplanes powered with Pratt and Whitney R-985 engines, a two-thousand-gallon-tank truck, a pick-up truck, two drivers and a flagman. A mixture of oil and 2,4-D is sprayed from twenty-six nozzles in the underside of the lower wing and is controlled from the open cockpit.

Two flagmen, one of them the extra pilot, take their positions at opposite ends of the field. They hold aloft white flags on ten-foot poles as markers for the pilots. As the planes complete each swath across the field, the flagmen shift their positions to mark the next swath. The two planes, one following the leader and a little to one side, fly two to ten feet above the grain. At the end of the swath one makes a sharp turn to the right, the other to the left and return to the strip indicated by the flagmen who often have to drop flat on their bellies to avoid the oncoming planes. And so, like shuttles in a loom, the pilots weave back and forth until they are forced to land for fuel or spray solution or a hurried lunch.

One of Pratt's pilots, who has been spraying and dusting since his discharge from the Air Force in 1947, said in a recent interview, "It's a cinch to fly the flat plains of Kansas but excuse me from Pennsylvania where I did several spraying jobs. There many of the fields are lined with telephone and power lines that you can't always see. Once on a job in that Quaker state I tore out three power lines and had to fly home with long streamers of wire trailing behind me. A refrigerating plant was without juice for nearly five hours. The furious owners sent a bill to my boss."

The Department of Agriculture, through the Federal States Co-operative Program, is working eastward in its fight against the Gypsy moth. In 1958 four hundred thousand acres were sprayed in Pennsylvania and, with the new insecticide, Sevin, 75,000 acres in New York State during 1959. It is expected that in a few years New England will have been covered. The fight against the perennial grasshopper goes on, as always, in the range lands of the West. The Forestry Service continues work on spruce budworm control in the West, 5,000,000 acres having been sprayed in 1958 and about 3,000,000 in 1959. DDT is used for the Gypsy moth and the budworm, and Aldrin, a formulated oil solution, for the grasshopper. The Mediterranean fruit fly, discovered in Florida in 1956, has been eradicated since November, 1957. A new program involving nine southeastern states has been started against the Imported Fire Ant, a granulated insecticide being used to reach the insects in their soil-inhabiting form. The Pink Bollworm in Arizona, once cleaned out, returned in 1958; 11,000 acres were sprayed for it in 1958 and 150,000 to 200,000 acres in 1959. Some work on the Japanese beetle in Illinois was completed in the spring of 1959, and Mormon crickets were sprayed in Utah, Nevada, and Idaho in 1958, and in Idaho and Wyoming in 1959.

Many planes used are now out of production: the Stearman biplane, always famous in this field; the C-46; the Boeing B-17 flying fortress; the Douglas B-18, an old bomber; the C-47; and even the DC-3, in a final stage of its long usefulness. The Fairchild Packet, or Flying Boxcar, has been used for some years. Piper Cubs are also used, and helicopters, the Hiller H-12 and the Bell-47. The Martin TBM, a war surplus torpedo bomber, has been added. A number of new aircraft, designed for this work, are the AG-2 from Transland, California; the Snow S-1 and S-2, built in Texas; the Grumman AG Cat; the Clark, from the company of that name; a Piper especially for dusting; the Pawnee from Rawdon, in Kansas; and the Call Company's Callair, Wyoming.

The insect killer is confronted by a problem that is unknown to the weed killer. Certain insects deposit their eggs on the *underside* of the leaves where they are protected from the falling droplets of lethal spray.

For a while the insect pests had the sprayers and dusters baffled, until it was discovered that the downward air stream created by the rotor of the helicopter rebounded vertically on striking the ground. Here was the answer to getting at the underside of the foliage with the lethal chemical.

A few months ago I watched, fascinated, a shuttling helicopter smother an extensive cranberry bog under billowing clouds of chemical vapor. More leisurely than the conventional plane, it looked as if it were invented for exactly that purpose. A foreman, an old hand in the berry business, said to me, "Wonderful gadgets, these 'copters.' They can do the job cheaper, quicker and better than we could do it on the ground."

CHAPTER FOUR

Business takes to the air

Big business has long since taken to the air. Industrial and commercial concerns own and operate planes for the use of executives hurrying to directors' meetings, sales conferences and divers assemblies in distant places where the presence of top brass seems to be obligatory. An important executive of a New York manufacturing concern said to me during an interview:

"When we first considered purchasing a plane, I was strongly opposed to the idea. The state of the market at that moment did not warrant such a large expenditure. I was voted down; the plane was purchased.

"Less than a month after we had acquired our DC-3, the purchasing agent of our largest customer came to our office to discuss an order that involved several million dollars. When we had discussed the transaction for an hour or so, it became evident that there were several points that would have to be considered by his board of directors. 'When is your next board meeting?' I asked.

"'At four this afternoon,' he replied, 'and it will be a month before the directors meet again.'

"It was ten-fifteen by the clock on my desk. For a moment I had visions of our strongest competitor walking away with the order. To reach Chicago by train would take eighteen or more hours of valuable time. There was little chance of securing a seat on a commercial airliner. It was my secretary who suggested using the company plane. Having opposed its purchase, I was hesitant about taking the suggestion.

" 'If you start now, you'll be in time for the meeting in Chicago. Shall I order the plane to be in readiness at Newark Airport?' The secretary's voice had a note of urgency in it, and then there was the large order teetering in the balance.

" 'Very well,' I said. 'Go ahead and order it.'

"It still lacked five minutes of eleven when the purchasing agent, my secretary and I boarded the plane. I was astonished at the charming yet practical simplicity of its appointments. The forward part of the cabin was an office in miniature. Desk, a few comfortable chairs, a brand-new typewriter and, if you please, an inviting sofa on which a work-weary executive might snatch a much needed hour's sleep. The afterpart of the cabin had the usual arrangement of seats to be found in commercial passenger planes.

"Airborne in a few minutes, the customer and I resumed our discussion. Meanwhile the nimble fingers of the secretary tapped out on the typewriter sundry clauses of the contract that was in the making. Too busy to enjoy the ever-changing panorama seven thousand feet below, we were unconscious of the rapidity with which time slipped by.

"It was with a feeling of awe rather than surprise that I saw the illuminated sign over the cockpit door flash its message: 'No smoking. Please adjust your safety belt.' A glance through the window revealed Lake Michigan spread out like a grayish blue carpet, its edge embroidered in a fantastic pattern that might have been designed by a cubist. It was the thrilling, bustling city of Chicago. When our wheels had touched the runway, I looked at my watch. It was three-twenty.

"As I left the directors' meeting several hours later with the coveted contract in my briefcase, my jubilation was dulled by a strange sense of guilt. The plane, to the purchase of which I had so strongly objected, had more than paid for itself."

During a recent visit to an internationally known maintenance plant, I saw a two-motor plane on the ramp in front of a large hangar. It glistened like a fresh-caught salmon in the sunlight. It had just been subjected to a complete overhaul and was ready for testing. Nearby stood the proprietor of the plant. There was a trace of Scottish burr in his speech as he informed me that the plane was owned by one of the large oil companies.

It had seen long and hard service but not once in its five years had it ever failed or faltered. Because of its reliability the president of the company had affectionately christened it "Old Faithful." However, hard wear and thousands of flight hours take their toll.

"When we began to disassemble the plane," he commented, "we discovered that there would have to be many replacements, engines, props, landing gear and several other essentials, to say nothing of interior decorating, upholstering and refurnishing."

"That must have been rather costly for the owners," I remarked.

"Well," said the plant proprietor, "that depends on how you look at it. The overhaul job has cost the owners about sixty thousand dollars, but a new plane of the same general type would cost about one hundred and fifty thousand."

"That makes for expensive travel," I ventured.

"Again it all depends on the viewpoint," he replied. "What you consider expense, those large companies look on as sound investment."

The executive vice president of a large corporation told me recently that if for any reason the company were deprived of the use of its planes, drastic changes would have to be made in the setup of its management. Many heads of big enterprises have their own private planes which they use for business as well as for pleasure.

One of Britain's largest newspaper publishers maintained a lavish residence in the British West Indies. In his frequent trips from his island home to the United States he used a sumptuously equipped Grumman Mallard. Vitally interested in the sources of his paper supply, he cruised indeed over thousands of miles of timberland in northern Canada and saw at first hand the extent of the growing raw material that some day would be the paper fed to his presses. The Grumman Mallard was the world's most advanced development of the amphibian plane, a type which is equally at home on land or water. This qualification had made it popular among private owners since landing facilities were increased immeasurably. When flying over most of the United States and Canada, the amphibian plane was rarely out of sight of a suitable landing place either on *terra firma* or water.

After a careful survey of the planes of the world, King Farouk of Egypt purchased two Mallards for his private use. The interior decoration and embellishment of those planes surpassed in richness and beauty anything so far attempted in a plane; they contained all the comforts and luxuries found in the most lavish home.

In the prewar period the yacht *Nourmahal*, a giant among pleasure craft, was a frequent visitor to the harbors of the world. Built at a cost of several million dollars, she was the last word in luxury ocean travel. Despite her great size and a crew of some sixty people, her accommodations were limited to a mere handful of guests. When war came, her owner turned her over to the United States Government. Notwithstanding her service in mid-Atlantic, ostensibly as a weather ship but actually as an important unit in the submarine warfare, she slipped into obscurity at the end of the conflict. Her former owner meanwhile seems to have had a change of heart. No longer did a floating palace with its retinue of retainers appeal to him. Instead he chose to travel and to entertain his guests in a Mallard, in which a crew of two sufficed, that could log off two hundred and twenty miles in the same time it took his yacht with all its horsepower and all its manpower to sail eighteen miles. As a gesture of affection for his former ship, however, he named his winged yacht the *Flying Nourmahal*.

Another of our great men in the world of finance took to the air in a really big way. Desiring spacious accommodations for his guests and himself, he purchased a Corsair, one of the larger and more successful airliners. The initial cost of this luxury ship was half a million dollars. Remodeling the interior to include three bedrooms, each with an adjoining bathroom, a spacious and sumptuously furnished salon and a score of refinements not to be found in commercial planes cost him another hundred thousand. While such lavish expenditure on personal aircraft is rare, many industrial concerns have much larger investments in their company fleets.

Douglas Aircraft Company used one of its Super-DC-3s in a dual capacity, as transportation for executives on business missions and as a "demonstrator" to enable prospective purchasers to observe and appraise its actual performance.

It was some time ago that I had a most dramatic experience in which the Super-DC-3 played an important role. Desirous of meeting the chief engineer of the Douglas company, I discussed the matter with E. Theodore Stern, Director of Public Relations, for the same company, in his New York office.

"It can be arranged very easily," said Stern. "I have invited a few business friends to lunch. Burton will be present. I'll see to it you have ample opportunity to talk with him if you would like to join us."

"I will be delighted," I said. "When and where do we meet?"

"Can you be at LaGuardia Airport at ten o'clock Thursday morning?"

The idea of luncheon at such an early hour mystified me a little. "Did you say *ten* o'clock?" I inquired.

"Yes. We'll hop up to Montreal. I know a delightfully quaint restaurant a few miles outside the city."

Unaccustomed to a journey of nearly four hundred miles to lunch, I had some misgivings. They disappeared quickly, however, on Thursday morning after the twenty-five-minute drive from my home to the airport. There in the waiting room of Colonial Air Lines I met my host and the other guests. Outside in the bright sunlight stood the Super-DC-3, her sides glistening like polished silver. A descendant of the world's most popular transport plane, the DC-3, it showed in every line, every curve and fairing. Animal lovers call it "breeding." Designed to accommodate thirty to thirty-seven passengers, the interior is a masterpiece of good taste in decoration; the individual seats have a cushiony comfort rarely found in domestic furniture.

Seated with Chief Engineer Burton, I began a barrage of questions that brought prompt answers, each more informative than the last. One of the world's greatest aviation engineers, he described the genesis of a plane in lan-

guage so simple and so understandable that sometimes it
was difficult to associate him with the huge aggregation
of brain power of which he is the directing head and moving spirit.

Although we were flying at eight thousand feet and
with perfect visibility, I was so fascinated by what this
master engineer had to say I did not get even a glimpse of
the cities and hamlets, the lakes and rivers and forests over
which we were passing. It seemed as if we had been airborne less than half an hour when he said, "We are approaching Montreal." I glanced through the window. We
were over the St. Lawrence River and already losing altitude. In a few moments our wheels touched the runway,
one hour and thirty-two minutes after leaving New York.

During lunch I discovered that our flight to Montreal
was not just a pleasure jaunt. It was in fact a performance
demonstration. Several of the guests were officials of an
airline that had under consideration the purchase of several Super-DC-3s.

On the return trip to New York I chatted with the
hostess of the plane. She told me of a little episode that
emphasized the growing trend of conducting business in
the air. It seems that a week or so before this luncheon
trip to Montreal, the hostess decided to fly to her home in
Buffalo to spend her two days' leave with her parents. It
is the custom in some airlines to extend to employees free
transporation when there are unsold seats in a plane.
This is known as traveling "deadhead." At the end of her
stay in Buffalo she went to the airport, confident there
would be a vacant seat on some plane bound for New
York. Luck was against her. All planes New York-bound
were sold out. There seemed to be no alternative but to
return by train, a long and expensive journey.

While considering her dilemma, she noticed four men
walking toward a private plane that seemed to be ready

to take off. One of them recognized her as the hostess on planes in which he had previously flown. He introduced his companions, one of whom he addressed as "General." After chatting a few moments she told of her predicament. "Think nothing of it," said the General. "We're flying to New York. Glad to give you a lift."

Thanking him and the others, the hostess accepted. With old-fashioned gallantry she was escorted to a seat in the waiting plane. Magazines and other reading matter were supplied her. A steward was instructed to see that she was made comfortable. Then the men went to the forward part of the plane which was fitted out as a luxurious office. Soon they were deep in a recapitulation of the day's business. During the journey the hostess, despite her interest in what she was reading, could not help overhearing snatches of the jargon of big business, finance, plant management, raw materials, delivery dates, demands of labor, antitrust laws, taxes and a hundred business minutiae that were as Sanskrit to her. Occasionally the General in his bluff and hearty manner would bellow, "How are you doing, young lady?" and then would proceed with the business at hand.

Not until they had reached the environs of New York City at sundown when lights in streets and avenues and millions of stores and homes spread a jeweled carpet under them, did the business-weary men relax and take their seats in which safety belts were adjusted. Only then did the girl, the trained hostess, learn from one of her air escorts that the handsome silver-haired general was none other than General Somervell who in World War II was the Lord Bountiful who kept millions of men supplied with what it takes to win a war. On his retirement from the armed forces, General Somervell became president of one of the country's most vital industrial corporations.

In spite of the fact that on our return journey from

Montreal we found it necessary to land at Bennington, Vermont, for customs and immigration inspection, which took about twelve minutes, we reached LaGuardia Airport in an hour and a half flying time. On reaching my home it occurred to me that I had traveled nearly eight hundred miles to my luncheon date in Canada and return but that it had taken only slightly more time than my weekly luncheons at the Dutch Treat Club in New York City twenty miles away. Such is the miracle of modern air transport.

An excellent example of how our industries profit by speedy transportation is found in the case of the Alaskan fish canneries. Each season for many years it was the custom of the canners to transport by steamer one thousand fishermen from Oakland, Seattle and other West Coast communities to Kaknek in the Aleutians. It was a slow and sometimes uncertain process.

Today the fishermen are flown to the fishing port by Trans-Ocean Airlines under contract with the employers who save more than fifty thousand man hours by the operation. At the end of the season these men who went down to the sea on wings, are flown back to the United States.

From its earliest days aviation has caught public imagination. Even today few can resist a glance at a plane as it streaks over city or village or farm. In the busiest metropolitan areas necks are craned and faces upturned to catch a fleeting glimpse of a passing plane. Only a few years ago a pilot friend flew me over New York City. The purpose of the flight was to enable me to secure some unusual aerial photographs of the incredible city. The weather was perfect, the light was excellent. The Empire State Building towering more than a hundred stories above the street, beckoned us while we were still many miles away. Only from the air can one conceive its vast bulk. To get the desired perspective, light and composition, it was necessary to circle the building several times while on a rather sharp bank that placed me in the low side of the plane. The broad sidewalks in the vicinity had their usual complement of hurrying pedestrians.

My attention, however, was concentrated on the building and the wonderful play of light and shadow on its stone and stainless steel. When we had circled half a dozen times or more while I made a number of shots, I awoke to the fact that we had a large audience. For several blocks the sidewalks were packed with people. The thousands of upturned faces looked like pink polka dots on a vari-colored background. Then it occurred to me what an excellent advertising medium our plane would have made since it forced the rapt attention of thousands, many of whom would tell in office and home many versions of the spectacle they had witnessed.

Undoubtedly this strange fascination or "eye appeal" of a plane in flight has been the basis on which a substantial aerial advertising business has been built. In World War I, millions of propaganda leaflets were broadcast over enemy territory from planes and with good results. Those scraps of paper contained advertising in the truest sense; they were designed to sell a single commodity—PEACE. Floating down from the skies and picked up to be read surreptitiously, they insured reader interest, the first essential of effective advertising.

During the years that intervened between the two great wars and more particularly, during the period of the business depression many pilots and plane owners saw an opportunity to earn at least an honest living in aerial advertising. Old planes were rolled out from hangars where they had lain idle for years. A quick overhaul job, a dash of paint, a renewed license, a little high-pressure salesmanship and they were in business. The cost of the particular advertising device to be used in conjunction with the plane was often defrayed by the advertiser. The pilot or pilot owner sold only his time and his skill and a loosely guaranteed circulation of thousands or millions of people to whom the advertiser's message would be delivered from the air.

Baseball and football games, conventions, seaside resorts and indeed any place where large numbers of people assembled out of doors became fertile ground in which the seeds of future sales were planted by the aerial advertising.

One of the earlier devices was a hundred-foot streamer on which was emblazoned in huge skeleton letters the name of the advertised product and a short word of praise. Supported by the slip stream of the plane which was towing it, the streamer held the attention of the throngs who saw it flutter by.

People in many of the larger cities were dismayed and perhaps a bit disgruntled at the sight of a huge illuminated billboard trundling across the night sky. Its lurid letters of light, blinking against the darkness, told of the virtues of a patent medicine or the deliciousness of a popular beverage. The plane, bearing the advertisement on the under side of its wings, was no war relic operated on a shoestring. Its electric power plant, supplying current to hundreds of electric bulbs, and the complex wiring system integrated in the plane's structure represented a considerable expenditure; the engineering of the installation was no mean project. Of the hordes who witnessed the night flights of the winged advertisement, very few gave a thought to whence the plane had come or where it would go when its night's work had been finished.

As a measure of economy, these ballyhoo planes base at remote fields frequently without tower or directing radio and, often as not, without even rudimentary border lights. In broad daylight and in clear weather such fields are adequate for take-off or landing by a skilled pilot. In darkness or fog, however, every landing is a gamble with the odds in favor of catastrophe.

One evening while the flying billboard was cruising in clear weather over the congested areas of New York City, an unpredicted fog rolled in from the ocean. Fearing a difficult landing, the pilot laid his course for the airfield thirty miles to the east on Long Island. With each mile covered the fog became denser. Without radio and flying by dead reckoning the pilot, an ex-barnstormer, was aided occasionally by a fleeting glimpse of the ground. While several miles from the landing field he had to skim over treetops and housetops with but inches to spare.

Then as the fog settled on the ground like a wet blanket, a shadowy mass flitted like a ghost under his left wing. In a fleeting glance he recognized it as the only silo for miles around. His heart skipped a beat when he remembered that it was several miles south of the field. Pulling back on the stick, he climbed up into the impenetrable void.

Like many of the daredevil pilots of his era, he had scant knowledge of instrument flying. Besides, his instrument board was equipped only with the barest essentials, compass, altimeter, artificial horizon, tachometer, engine temperature and fuel gauge. His fleeting glimpse of the silo had told him his landing field lay to the north. As he changed his course, the wet darkness seemed to grow denser. When instinct told him he was in the vicinity of the field, he circled to a lower altitude. The altimeter showed an approximate one hundred feet. For a moment a diffused halo of sickly light below him appeared and disappeared. He reasoned that it was an automobile on the highway that bordered the field. Cutting his engine down almost to the stalling point, he pressed the stick gently forward. "Here goes for a landing!" he said through clenched teeth.

Almost instantly from under the belly of the plane came a rending noise as the landing wheels tore through a cluster of telephone wires. It was followed by a series of sickening jolts; a wing tip plowed the soil, throwing the plane into a murderous ground loop that ended by standing the plane on its nose for a short instant, then flopping it wearily over on its back.

When the pilot regained consciousness, he was hanging head downward, suspended from his seat by his safety belt. Although too dazed to release himself, he recognized the voice of a farmer who lived close to the airfield, saying to another, "Of all the danged fools!—flyin' on a night like this!"

That was the last of the flying billboard ever seen by the craning crowds in the Metropolis. Its end was not unlike that of its ill-fated predecessor, a flying boat that made a single sky trip, flashing a nationally known trademark.

Back in the Twenties a small group of aviation enthusiasts pooled their resources in fitting out a superannuated but staunch flying boat with the heavy equipment necessary to operate some hundreds of twenty-five-watt lamps which formed the flashing aerial sign. A member of the courageous little band told me recently that all but the pilot's cockpit was lined with storage batteries. The idea of advertising in the sky was so novel in those days that the promoters had no difficulty in signing up an advertiser at a substantial figure. On the night of the plane's premier flight the advertiser, a few friends and the owners of the aircraft watched the proceedings from the roof of a mid-town hotel. The pilot, knowing he was being observed by the sponsor, circled overhead, dipped his wings in salute and continued on his advertising mission.

Several hours later while the sponsor and his party were celebrating the success of the venture and prophesying a bright future, one of the owners of the plane was called to the phone. The call came from Rockaway where the plane was based; the pilot was on the wire. "Hello, Bob," he said in a tremulous voice, "I have bad news."

Knowing the pilot to be a perfectionist, Bob replied, "Forget it! Run the plane into the hangar and join the party! You did a swell job. Our sponsor is tickled to death."

After a moment's silence the pilot, his voice still shaky, croaked, "Listen! You may as well know the worst. After a perfect landing I struck a floating log. The old crate ripped open from nose to tail and sank in forty feet of water."

And so a dream of wealth garnered in the night sky lies buried in the Atlantic.

Another variation of aerial advertising made its appearance in metropolitan areas a few years ago. Its appeal was to the ear rather than to the eye. It consisted of a phonograph and public-address system installed in a plane. Its method was patterned after that adopted by many radio stations; to arrest public attention by music that ranged from Bach to swing with frequent interruptions for "commercials" lauding the products of the sponsors. Powerful amplication hurled its music and messages earthward in an ear-splitting avalanche of sound. It was short-lived, however.

One summer evening while thousands were enjoying a symphony concert in New York's Lewisohn Stadium, strange dissonances came out of nowhere. The orchestra was rendering Mendelssohn's "Fingal's Cave." The beautiful rhythms of the opus soon became inextricably tangled with the blasting beat of a jazz band somewhere high in the darkness.

An audible ripple of resentment spread throughout the stadium. Here and there were shouts of anger and threatening fists were raised as the plane circled overhead while the man at the flying microphone gave his sponsors their money's worth. It developed later that neither the pilot nor the disc jockey was aware that a concert was in progress.

The next day complaints from the outraged listeners poured into City Hall. These grievances fell on sympathetic ears. The mayor, an ardent music lover, was also a militant advocate of noise abatement. An ordinance was passed prohibiting the use of advertising public-address systems on the streets or in the air over the city.

Many of the aerial advertising enterprises that sprouted during the last two decades failed for one reason or another, but chiefly because a plane flying, say, at a hundred miles an hour within the zone of visibility, gives the on-looker even with good eyesight only a short and ineffectual glimpse of the message it carries.

Skywriting on the other hand gives perfect visibility over an extensive area and is legible to tens or hundreds of thousands of people simultaneously. Indeed it has been classed by national advertisers as an effective and legitimate medium for localized advertising.

Without leaving my desk I have watched many times these writers in the sky emblazoning their silvery messages on the blue above distant New York City. And I have often sat in wonder at the mysteries of it. It was with keen pleasure, therefore, that I interviewed an executive of Skywriter Corporation and learned some of the amazing details of an amazing business.

It was on the battlefields of Europe in 1918 that the idea of writing across the sky came into being, when an English flier, Major Savage, was shot down. Wounded and with his plane in flames he managed to live through a crash landing. As he lay on the ground, he noticed a mile-long streamer of white smoke hanging in the sky where it had been left by his disabled plane during his fiery descent.

Soon after the cessation of hostilities Major Savage discovered that by injecting a liquid with a special oil base into the exhaust line of a plane, he could create a dense white smoke that retained its opaque quality for reasonably long periods. A skillful pilot, he soon learned the difficult art of writing with smoke. Coming to the United States in 1922, he greeted New Yorkers with the first message written across the sky. It read simply, "HELLO NEW YORK!" So successful was his demonstration, he had little difficulty in securing lucrative advertising contracts.

From that beginning with a single light plane, a British SE-5, was developed the Skywriter Corporation with its staff of specially trained pilots and a fleet of twenty planes flying in different parts of the United States. Except in rare instances only cities of fifty thousand population or over were considered suitable for a campaign of sky-writing.

Taking off from a nearby airfield, the skywriter flew to a designated area in which there was a dense population. When he had reached an altitude of ten thousand to fifteen thousand feet, he checked his oil flow with a smoke spurt or two and then began writing.

In order to be legible from the ground the letters must be formed backward and upside down. Each letter is nearly a mile from top to bottom, consequently the letter M requires about four miles of flying. Furthermore each of the lines that compose the letter must be separated at the meeting point by a space of seventy-five feet so that the slip stream from the propeller will not break up the smoke already laid. For instance, the top line of a T must be the height of a six-story building above the vertical stem. Perspective and the many miles from which it is seen close up the gap. Flying at 175 miles an hour calls for supreme skill on the part of the pilot.

As the jet of smoke leaves the plane, it has a diameter of six inches that expands gradually to about one hundred feet while a letter is being completed. The smoke is ejected from the plane's exhaust at a rate of a million cubic feet a minute. When flying at twelve thousand feet or more, the pilots use oxygen masks to make breathing easier.

Unpredictable winds are the enemy of aerial writers. A sudden gust in the high altitudes has been known to sweep an invisible eraser over the first letters of a word while the final letters were still being written. "It's all in the game," say the pilots philosophically.

Big events like baseball and football games became a fair target for the sky scriveners. During a famous World Series they wrote the score in smoke and gained the breathless thanks of millions of fans. On another occasion blasé New Yorkers were thrilled by a game of tick-tack-toe played two miles up by a pair of frolicsome skywriting pilots.

The daring, skill and good old-fashioned enterprise that built skywriting into a flourishing business have blazed a trail for others to follow, and now a new system of writing has been introduced. Known as "Skytyping," it is a mass production technique in which a squadron of seven planes operate simultaneously in forming the smoke letters. This insures rapid completion of the message and consequently a longer period of legibility.

While skywriting and skytyping appear to be closely related, actually they are only distant cousins. They differ in appearance, technique and in magnitude of operation. In skywriting a single plane lays down a trail of smoke in solid lines that may be straight or curved as the individual

letter requires. The letters of a skytyped message, however, consist of a series of gigantic smoke "dots" laid down
in straight lines. To accomplish this, seven planes fly
straight parallel courses with the "mother" plane in the
center. Each plane is equipped with a radio connected to
its smoke-making device. The radios are set to respond to
a predetermined number of impulses. The words to be
skytyped are set up in a pattern of electric switches on
the mother plane's control board. A master switch in
the lead plane sets contacts revolving. As each switch is
closed, impulses are transmitted to the radios in certain
of the other planes. Each impulse releases a gigantic puff
of smoke. In the letter T, for instance, seven puffs from
Number I plane form the cross stroke, while one puff
given off simultaneously from each of the other six planes
form the vertical stem of the letter.

Flying at 180 miles an hour, the seven AT-6s can type
a twenty-one-letter message fifteen miles long and a mile
high in five minutes. At an altitude of fifteen thousand
feet the message is visible in clear weather for a distance
of forty miles. This is not surprising since each dot contains about 350,000 cubic feet of chemical smoke.

In this newer form of aerial advertising the pilot's job
is an easy one. He simply flies a straight course; electronics does the rest.

Since advertising has become a several-billion-dollar
business in which innumerable arts, crafts, skills, industries and professions are engaged, it seems reasonable that
aviation should get its share. The first essential of a successful advertisement is that it compel attention from a
maximum number of potential purchasers of the product
advertised. In brief, it must catch the eye of the cus-
tomers. One of the most efficient of the eye-catching sky
media was the huge bulk of a one-time Navy dirigible nosing its way through the night sky while along its swollen

sides skittered flamboyant letters bearing the message of some expectant sponsor.

These night-prowling monsters were close kinfolk to the gigantic electric signs that have made the mid-town section of New York's Broadway world-famous as the Great White Way.

Dirigibles were then controlled by the old, established firm of Gordon Leigh, Incorporated. In an interview with them a number of years ago I learned that the company purchased from the United States Navy six of the mighty gas bags, for operation in various parts of the United States. Each of the "blimps," as they were erroneously called, bulked larger than a city block of six-story buildings. With a length of 265 feet and a height of about seventy feet, nearly half a million feet of helium gas were required to give it effective buoyancy. A single load of the nonflammable gas cost approximately $10,000. Despite the best efforts of builders, owners and crews, the normal leakage of gas necessitated a new load about once a year. Serious leakage was caused occasionally by nitwits in rural areas who used the dirigibles as targets for their rifle bullets.

Each dirigible carried a crew of four men, a chief pilot, a co-pilot, an engineer who was also a pilot and a rigger who supervised the complex mechanism that operated the electric letters along the sides of the ship.

One of the chief advantages of the lighter-than-air craft over the airplane was its speed range. During its journeys to and from its distant hangar, it could move along at a mile-a-minute clip. Arriving over its designated area of operation, it flew at a leisurely pace or hovered motionless over any desired spot.

Despite the spectacular character of the flying advertisement, it has contributed its share to building certain of the industries that have made America great.

Whether it advertises fuels or furs, soft drinks or United States bonds, the sky message spurs the sale of its sponsor's products. The fact that these hard-headed businessmen continue to spend large sums annually on aerial advertising is proof enough that it is profitable.

CHAPTER FIVE

Inside story: Berlin airlift

No story of aviation would be complete without at least an outline of the Berlin airlift. In the years to come it will be classed with the initial hop of the Wright brothers at Kitty Hawk, the Lindbergh flight to Paris, the world-circling nonstop flight of Lady Luck II and the other milestones in the history of human flight. Besides its heroisms, its enterprise and its dogged resolve in the face of obstacles that seemed insurmountable, it demonstrated the undreamed potentialities of the airplane in the field of freight transport.

In June, 1948, the Soviet Union clamped down on road and rail deliveries of essential commodities to West Berlin. Two and a half million people, cut off from their supplies of food, clothing and medicines, looked to America for relief. Besides the political aspects of the situation, a humanitarian duty was laid in the lap of the United States Military Command.

At first glance the task seemed hopeless. The only route over which supplies could be transported to the city was by air through three narrow corridors agreed on by treaty. Never had such a vast transport problem confronted aviation, military or civilian.

85

General Lucius Clay, the United States Military Governor and his British and French associates computed that by a tightening of belts and rigorous self-control the Berlin population could be supported on 4,500 tons of food and fuel daily.

To General LeMay was assigned the problem of organizing the airlift, later to be known as Operation "Vittles." Utilizing only the handful of Douglas C-47s he had available, the lift got underway from the Wiesbaden Air Force base. Grounded fliers were plucked from their desks. Pilots from Alaska to Australia were alerted. Word went out to the four corners of the aviation world that tough-fibered men were wanted for a man's job. Planes and more planes, the bigger the better, were also needed.

To thousands of pilots and airmen the call was a challenge that snatched them from their homes and jobs and sent them winging to the strangest mission of their careers, the "LeMay Coal and Feed Run," a round-the-clock grind with no foreseeable end.

On the first day of the airlift eighty tons of supplies, mostly milk for children, were flown into Berlin's Tempelhof Airdrome. A bit discouraging, it was the modest acorn from which grew the mighty oak. During the six weeks that followed, each minute became a hectic one. Rain, mist, freezing cold and flying hours beyond human endurance nicknamed the venture Operation "Nightmare." Lieutenant Murphy flew nine hours, had duty nineteen and slept seven. Captain Kolch flew eight, had duty for sixteen hours and slept eight. And that is the way it went week in and week out. And yet, only one of that hardy band collapsed under the strain; his nerves could not adjust themselves to the weather and the instrument flying and the soul-searching ordeal of GCA.

Ground Control Approach is the seeing eye that leads planes blinded by heavy fog to a safe landing on an appointed runway. It is one of the applications of the miracle radar to safety at sea, on land and in the air.

A controller, seated before three radar scopes resembling circular television screens, scans the murky sky for approaching planes. Suddenly a tiny pip of light appears on one of the scopes. It is a plane eight miles distant and at an altitude of ten thousand feet. The controller's job now is to guide the plane to a prearranged glide path.

On contact with the tower the plane's pilot turns over to GCA. When about four miles distant, the plane begins its descent as if it were following an invisible string that led in a straight line to the touchdown point. He obeys every order and direction given by the controller who is following the course of the pip of light on the scope.

With good voice, accurate speech and a smooth calm manner, the man on the ground keeps the blinded pilot informed constantly: "Sixty-five degrees; altitude ten thousand; gear down; flaps set; increase rate of descent; azimuth good; elevation good; doing fine; fifty feet over runway; ready for touchdown point; take over."

As the plane reaches the end of the glide path, its wheels touch the runway. The pilot takes a long breath. Another plane has come safely into the invisible airport.

During the weeks that followed, each hour brought reinforcements of men and planes and a set determination to see it through. Eventually planes were arriving over Tempelhof Airdrome at less than three-minute intervals in a deadly game of Follow-the-Leader. Hour after hour, day and night, the roar of the passing planes reverberated over Berlin.

At first there was some confusion, due largely to intolerable flying weather and the highly restricted air space. Flying the narrow corridors at such short intervals created traffic problems never encountered on private lines. Due to the pounding resulting from the incessant landing of overloaded planes, landing gear and nose-wheels required constant maintenance, tire and brake consumption was four to five times greater than was expected. A flat tire meant the disruption of the split-second dispatching program.

For instance: One night while a Douglas C-54 was almost ready for the final turn one thousand feet above the Tempelhof rotunda, the pilot, peering down at the lighted field, watched a heavily loaded Skymaster settle down on the concrete runway, lurch heavily and come to a stop a quarter of the way down the strip.

The landing lights on the next plane in line behind the disabled Skymaster shot skyward as the pilot climbed for another pass at the field. The Douglas pilot followed suit as did the others in his rear. Immediately radio headsets in approaching planes began to crackle with instructions: "Tempelhof Tower to all cargo planes: Cargo aircraft on runway with two blown tires. Maintain intervals and continue on present course."

Eighteen planes answered, "Roger."

Soon Tempelhof had twenty-one planes "stacked" at different altitudes in the darkness above the field to a height of nearly ten thousand feet. The roar of eighty-four engines in the treacherous merry-go-round made an uninterrupted roll of thunder. Every few minutes instructions from the tower added another plane to the "stack." In the dimly lit cockpits of each plane the tension became unbearable as crews sweated it out until traffic had resumed its normal course.

Fog was the implacable enemy of pilots and ground forces alike. Occasionally a curtain of pea soup rolled in over the area of operations. Then men prayed for a modicum of luck to mix with their skill. Despite all the advances science has made, a landing in a zero fog is still a nerve-wracking experience. While the pilot gives his best, he also hopes for the best.

One September day a thick fog rolled in on Tegel airlift base so suddenly that a loaded Skymaster which was seen to land safely, was soon lost in the maze of taxi-strips and runways. The pilot asked for instructions from the tower. But a plane lost on the field was a brand-new problem to the tower. A "follow me" jeep was sent out to search for the Skymaster. A few minutes after its departure the jeep too became hopelessly lost.

By a process of guidance and guesswork from the control tower, the Skymaster was led blindfolded to her appointed position on the unloading strip. Two hours later the "follow me" jeep crawled home from its fruitless search.

April 15, 1949, stands out as a red-letter day. Since the next day would be Easter Sunday, the men of the Airlift established what long will be remembered as their "Easter Parade." They vowed to deliver at least ten thousand tons of supplies to the city. No one, especially the communications men, will ever forget that memorable twenty-four hours. In the middle of the afternoon there was a commotion in the Air Safety Center where controllers representing American, British, French and Russian air forces kept track of all aircraft crossing the city. All day the air throbbed with the incessant roar of planes; the Easter Parade was in its stride. The controllers at the board were straining every nerve posting the cards that represented each of the aircraft arriving and departing from the four lift terminals at thirty-second intervals.

The Soviet member of the four-man team soon became bewildered by the rapidity with which the others carried on the posting. Suddenly he threw his hands in the air and complained bitterly to the American officer on duty. "Your planes are coming in and out too fast. I cannot keep track of them!" Then he strode from the room. With sly grins of elation the other controllers continued to post the identifying cards with increased tempo.

By the end of the twenty-four-hour period Operation "Vittles" had demonstrated the potentialities of the Combined Airlift Task Force. The Easter Parade delivered 12,940 tons of supplies to the beleaguered city in 1,398 flights between noon of April fifteenth and noon the following day.

Strenuous as the work was, there were moments when the iron discipline became frayed at the edges. Weary, sleep-starved men sometimes filled the ether with jibes and gripes until interrupted by, "Tower to all aircraft: Maintain radio silence, please. Must contact other aircraft arriving." Even the tower had its off moments as witness the experience of an eager young pilot.

"I was all ready to enter the pattern," he said. "I called the tower for instructions. The reply was all garbled. It sounded like Russian. I kept repeating my call over and over, 'Tower from Big Willie 405. You are coming in garbled. Please repeat!'

"The jabberwocky from the tower continued. My insistent requests to repeat brought no improvement. Finally a new voice came on loud and clear. The operator gave me my final instructions and apologized for the poor reception. 'You see,' he said, 'you were speaking with Sergeant O'Connor. He had just lost the upper plate of his false teeth in a sneeze and could not talk. Sorry!' "

So great was the speed and so short the time between landings and take-offs that the pilots at the Wiesbaden supply base were known to taxi to the run-up position with the entire tie-down crew and cargo handlers still on board. This hectic pace continued for 321 days and nights of the blockade. By the time Air Force Lieutenant Joe Russo brought the last airlift plane to a landing in Berlin, the very last plane to fly the Russian blockade, the airlift had transported cargo that equaled the capacity of sixteen thousand fifty-car railroad trains or a total of 1,588,293 tons.

To accomplish this took more than 936,000 individual flights. The planes traveled 87,500,000 miles on the three narrow air corridors into Berlin. An average of 250 aircraft flew their appointed rounds day and night, logging more than 413,000 hours. Navy tankers shuttled the Atlantic to deliver 112,000,000 gallons of high octane gasoline to the sky trucks that kept a city from starving.

Cold figures give but a vague idea of the strains and tensions undergone by men and planes. During eleven unforgettable months 53,000 people worked day and night to keep the airlift in perpetual motion. Thousands of trucks and trailers crowded the highways as they shuttled, round the clock, between planes and supply depots.

Two and a half million people who but recently had called us "enemy" now greeted us as friends. Crowds of them gathered daily here and there throughout the city to watch the lifesaving airplanes come and go. Now and then cardboard boxes of candy were dropped by the fliers for distribution among the wide-eyed children.

Real reward came later when a prominent Berliner said to an exhausted group of pilots, "We feel that God sent you American fliers to us at this time to teach us how wrong we were ever to fight a war with you."

That sentence alone was worth every penny of the $149,600,000 the airlift cost the United States.

CHAPTER SIX

The helicopter comes of age

With the helicopter, that most versatile vehicle ever conceived by man, now rapidly becoming turbine-powered, carrying guided missiles and geodetic dome shelters, helping construct high-tension power lines, and reaching the hitherto inaccessible places of earth for purposes of industry or rescue, it is hard to realize that it was only twenty years ago, on September 14, 1939, that Igor Sikorsky demonstrated to the world that a "flying machine" could raise itself vertically by its bootstraps, fly sideways and backward, and hover motionless as a dragonfly over a waterlily.

I remember well one glorious morning at Bridgeport, Connecticut. I had just finished a lengthy interview with Igor Sikorsky, who may be truthfully styled the "Dean of Aeronautical Science." He had just completed and actually flown the miracle machine that seemed to defy the laws of gravity and aerophysics. As I was about to leave, he said in his most gracious manner, "Perhaps you would like to see a motion picture of the machine in its first flight." He called it a machine rather than a plane or helicopter.

When I said I would be delighted, he asked his assistant

92

Ivan to get the film projector and screen in readiness. Soon I was ushered into a darkened room adjoining the Sikorsky sanctum. The silence was broken only by the whirr of the projector. Up to that moment I knew only in a vague way what a helicopter looked like. A little shocked I saw a skeleton of steel tubing that had a slight resemblance to the stripped fuselage of a light plane. Its engine, starkly naked against the landscape, was connected with a horizontal rotor, the three blades of which suggested to me quills from the wing of a giant eagle. On its spiraling tail were two small propeller-like rotors. The strange contraption stood in the parking lot outside the factory and occupied the space of about three automobiles.

Sikorsky, the master who created it, climbed to the pilot's seat. Although exposed to the four winds, he wore a meticulously tailored business suit and a Homburg hat. The huge rotor above him began to revolve like the upper structure of a merry-go-round. When it had gained what seemed to be only moderate momentum, the weird-looking contraption rose vertically to a height of about fifty feet and there hovered motionless for a few moments as if trying to decide which way to fly. Then away it darted like a huge dragonfly, circling here and there over the ten-acre cabbage field, mounting with every revolution of its rotor.

Returning close to its starting point, it stopped in mid-air and hung suspended between earth and sky at a height of about a hundred feet. It was a startling demonstration of victory over gravity but it was as nothing when compared with what followed. First, it actually flew backward, a feat that even the eagle could not accomplish. Then it flew sideways, first to the right and then to the left without moving in a forward direction.

Then Ivan, the assistant, appeared on the screen, bearing a neat package that might have contained a week's laundry. He walked to the center of the cabbage patch and waited. Down from the sky swept the spraddling helicopter to a few feet from where Ivan stood. It stopped and remained motionless some five feet above the cabbages. Ivan ceremoniously handed the package to the master at the controls. In acknowledgment Sikorsky raised his hat with a flourish, after which he circled over the factory several times and landed in the tiny space from which he had taken off.

When the last foot of the film had flickered out, I felt as if I had witnessed a phenomenon as confounding as if I had seen the falls of Niagara tumbling upward.

Many months later when the helicopter had passed out of the fledgling state into full feather, I witnessed another demonstration of its victory over gravity. Now its skeleton fuselage was sheathed in aluminum, its cockpit domed in transparent plastic. It rested on two inflated pontoons. A licensed pilot rather than its inventor was at the controls. Its bulbous forepart and spindling tail gave it the appearance of a giant tadpole. As it took to the air, its whirling rotor seemed to lift it with greater ease. In full flight its speed seemed to have increased far beyond that of its prototype that I had seen on the screen.

Its first demonstration was a vertical landing between the high banks of a water-filled gully not much larger than the helicopter itself. As if gathering its breath for its next flight, its rotor blades circled at a leisurely speed. Then its engine roared. Under the whip of one hundred horsepower the rotating pinions resumed their merry-go-round at a speed that made their tips invisible. The cyclonic downdraft churned the water into concentric ripples of foam.

Airborne, it made a beeline toward the factory of its birth to give further proof of its ability to land in places and spaces that forever will be beyond the accomplishment of wingborne planes. The increasing demand for runways of two or more miles testifies to this.

Among the more startling feats was a perfect landing on a pile of wooden engine crates stacked to the height of a two-story building. The top of the pile was about ten feet square, scarcely large enough to accommodate the pontoons. When immediately over the improvised platform, the helicopter became static. Then gently as a falling petal its pontoons rested on the wooden pile. That occurred only eighteen years ago.

Probably no branch of aviation has had so phenomenal a growth in so short a period of time. From being a seven-day wonder the helicopter passed rapidly into its present position of all-round worker and stand-by, almost incredibly versatile in its usefulness. Men have always dreamed of such a creature, hovering above the earth and dipping down whenever and wherever needed.

It is best known for its military and naval uses and for the heroic role it plays in crisis and disaster, but its multiple other tasks, in industry and adventure, are almost beyond enumeration. It not only flies wounded men to hospital and snatches downed pilots from icy seas or No-man's land, as it did in Korea, but it battles crop-destroying pests; it is indispensable in offshore drilling for oil; it herds cattle and finds lost sheep; and inspects thousands of miles of high-tension wires. Now it is helping to construct these same high-tension power lines ("Helicopters in power line construction saved us months in time and up to 60 per cent in costs," says a utility official); is the ally of intricate building jobs in general; and is keeping pace with the swiftly expanding technical needs of the modern world in all its aspects.

In the mining field, prospecting is now being done from the air in this way, and because of the helicopter's range of speed from zero to more than a hundred miles an hour, explorers find it invaluable. In regions where archeological treasures are hidden by dense tropical vegetation, the powerful downdraft from the helicopter's rotor sweeps the curtain of foliage aside and reveals ruins which might otherwise go undiscovered for many more centuries.

I remember in the early days asking a pilot how it was possible for a helicopter to fly without wings.

"It doesn't," he said, "since each of its rotor blades is a true wing. It is the air moving across the wing surface of any type of plane that keeps it afloat. The contour of every wing is so designed that the air motion increases the air pressure on the lower side of the wing and reduces it above the upper surface of the wing. These unequal pressures cause the plane to rise into the low pressure area and so to give it 'lift.' The conventional plane cannot leave the ground until this lift is provided by the speed of its wings through the air during the take-off. The rotating wings of the helicopter create the necessary air movements across their surfaces and so lift is accomplished without forward speed. When the rotor blades or wings spin fast enough, the machine is lifted bodily into the air."

During the earlier experiments on the helicopter, he told me, it was found that "when it lifted itself into the air, the body, or fuselage, of the machine had a tendency to rotate in a direction opposite to that of the whirling rotor wings. This phenomenon known as 'torque' was conquered by Sikorsky when he placed a small propeller on one side of the tail.

"The helicopter moves forward, backward or crabwise by tilting the vertical rotor shaft in the direction in which the pilot wants to fly. The little propeller on the tail acts as a rudder which depends on its varying speeds for holding or changing the course of the machine."

The new SH-3A helicopter, built for the U. S. Navy by Sikorsky
Aircraft at Stratford, Connecticut, taxis in the water to demonstrate its universal landing capability. It has a flying boat hull
and retractable landing wheels, and can operate from land,
water, ice, snow, mud, or tundra. The SH-3A is powered by
twin gas-turbine engines. It is the Navy's first all-weather helicopter and its latest anti-submarine weapons system.

Coming in for a landing at New York's LaGuardia Airport, this Constellation has completed her flight from overseas. The landing wheels are retracted during flight.

A former U. S. Navy dirigible hovers over the nation's capital while engaged in its peacetime job of advertising an American product in the night sky.

American Airlines Jet-Powered Electra Flagship cruises at
410 miles an hour, is capable of speeds in excess of 450 miles
an hour. The Lockheed turboprop, American's short- and
medium-range airliner for the Jet Age, seats 68 passengers
in luxurious first-class accommodations. It also has a lounge
for relaxation, seating six.

The Port of New York Authority, operator of LaGuardia Airport, has under way a $115 million redevelopment program which includes a great new passenger terminal nearly seven times the size of the one it replaces. It will be completed in time for the opening of the New York World's Fair in 1964. An observation deck will run the entire length of the roof of the terminal and will provide visitors to the airport with an incomparable view of the more than 400 planes that use the airport facilities daily.

To the New York International Airport, spreading over 4,900 acres, giant planes from overseas are now homing every day. Photograph shows an American 707 Jet taxiing along a runway under which traffic moves unimpeded. Below the water level, the walls and floor of this underpass are eight feet thick to prevent flooding.

One of Pratt & Whitney Aircraft's new, small jet engines, the JT-12, weighs only 430 pounds and produces 3,000 pounds of thrust. It has been selected to power the Lockheed Jetstar, McDonnell Model 119, and North American Sabreliner as well as drones manufactured by Republic and Fairchild.

The Boeing B-52 Stratofortress, powered by eight Pratt and Whitney Aircraft J-57 turbojets. This long-range intercontinental bomber is regarded as the Air Force's "long rifle." It has a maximum speed of over 600 miles an hour and a service ceiling of over 40,000 feet. The gas-turbine engines are mounted in pods and suspended from the wings. This is used by the Strategic Air Command. Starters and fuel controls are furnished by Hamilton Standard.

The Sikorsky S-64 Skycrane's first flight took place May 9, 1962. This twin-turbine-powered helicopter can lift a wide variety of weights beneath its skeletal fuselage. It can carry a ten-ton pay-load, and is considered a "prime mover"—the aerial equivalent of railroad locomotives and truck tractors, for both military and industrial use. Above, the S-64 before loading; below, carrying pod.

Convair B-58 Hustler, the nation's first supersonic bomber, carries a detachable "pod" which permits it to perform a variety of missions.

The Convair Air Force long-range fighter, the F-102 Delta Dagger.

Here are the maintenance men on whom we ultimately depend for safety in air travel. The best engineering can be defeated by the faulty adjustment of a nut or a bolt or by the careless adjustment of a minor mechanism.

The Kaman Huskie, the H-43B, goes into service with the United States Air Force. It is powered by a Lycoming T-53 gas turbine engine. It comes equipped with hoist, litter racks and a specially designed fire-rescue kit, including 82 gallons of foam extinguishing chemical, hose, crowbars, axes, etc. Because it can search and rescue so effectively, unhampered by lack of roads, rough terrain and other hazards to ground travel, the H-43B is uniquely adapted to this job.

Only two years out of high school, this aeronautical engineering student has mastered many of the problems that will confront him later when he takes his place in one of the many divisions in the engineering department of an aircraft concern.

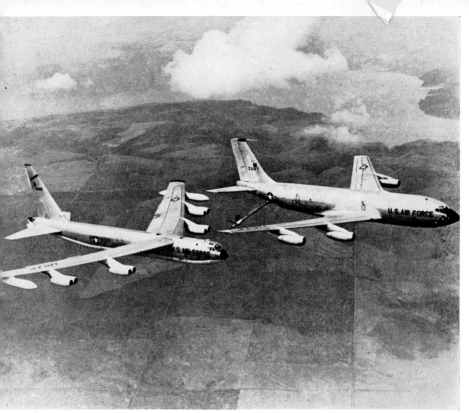

The Boeing KC-135 jet tanker, powered by four J-57 engines, refueling the Boeing B-52 Stratofortress.

Wrapped into this slim, razor-winged streak of fighting-power, the Lockheed F-104A Starfighter, is the greatest combination of speed and flying performance ever built into a combat airplane. Powered by the General Electric J-79 turbojet, producing higher thrust per pound of engine weight than any jet of its power class, this U. S. Air Force plane has been acclaimed as "the world's fastest fighter."

The helicopter carries most of its cargo externally, not within itself as do other carriers, picking up and transmitting objects of any bulk and from any location, weight being the only consideration. Progress in perfecting the helicopter has thus, of course, run along the lines of weight-lifting capacity. The Sikorsky S-56 for example, using Pratt and Whitney Aircraft R-2800 engines and a five-bladed rotor, was able to carry more weight than any before it.

Then came a radically new concept in aircraft design and use, the "Flying Crane," a machine with a skeletal fuselage and enormous weight-lifting capacity. The S-60 crane helicopter, demonstrated publicly for the first time in April, 1959, marked the start of a revolution in the transportation industry through its saving of time, money, and trouble. In that demonstration, just as a sample, the great crane lifted a two-ton utility pole and placed it neatly in a pre-dug hole; transported a 60-foot, 4,500-pound Army bridge span and positioned it on a foundation; and flew across the field carrying a dummy of the huge Honest John missile.

A newer crane model, the S-64 Skycrane, is powered with twin gas-turbine engines and carries a payload of up to ten tons. The pilot's (or co-pilot's) seat swivels 180 degrees, so he can fly the ship while facing rearward. This gives him a view from his glass enclosed cockpit of loading and unloading operations, so that he need not depend on directions from someone on the ground. The Skycrane can carry detachable vans for passenger, cargo or specialized use such as medical or communications facilities. Prefabricated houses and transmission towers will be among its fabulous freight, and bridges, roads, and rough terrain need no longer be considered obstacles. Detachable "pods" underhang the crane, for carrying passengers and cargo, bringing supplies, and evacuating victims.

Because of its life-saving properties, the helicopter

makes the headlines perhaps more frequently than any other type of aircraft. The exact kind of thing a helicopter is able to do, for instance in a flood disaster, is casually mentioned by one of the Sikorsky pilots at work in the hurricane-caused Connecticut flood that day in August, 1955: "We had been unloading the first of twenty-four people in a three-story house when it became apparent we weren't getting them out fast enough. We started grasping at ideas for completing the job before the house toppled. We waved them all to the top floor and then hovered alongside the window while they were helped into the cabin." Which is certainly one way in which a helicopter is an improvement on, say, the rowboat.

One pilot gives up and says only, "The flood was something you'd see only once in a lifetime. It isn't the sort of thing you can describe." It was, in short, the sort of thing which demanded not words but drastic action. By packing people into the limited space until the little helicopters "looked like subway cars at rush hour," evacuation was finished at just about dark. Those who couldn't get into the cabins were towed through the water on the end of a sling. "Several of the people we brought up that way cleared floating stuff in the nick of time."

There is of course nothing surprising in all this: it just happened that this particular rescue was nearer home than any of the other large-scale disasters which have now become classics. And luckily for Connecticut, the Sikorsky plant was only a stone's throw from the flood area: it was like calling on a neighbor. Some years ago (epics of the sea are timeless) the Coast Guard Air Station at Floyd Bennett Field was feverishly dismantling a helicopter for shipment by an Army C-54, while the Coast Guard Air Station at Elizabeth City, North Carolina, was dismantling another one, for shipment by another C-54—destination Gander Airport, Newfoundland. At Gander, reassembled, the two helicopters started off to pick up the survivors of a Belgian Sabena airliner bound from Ireland to New York which had crashed mysteriously in the Newfoundland wilderness, in a spot (discovered by a Coast Guard plane) from which only helicopters could rescue them. The helicopters in this case formed the last essential link in the lifesaving chain which finally deposited the litter-borne patients in the Gander hospital. The helicopters left the survivors (fourteen of the eighteen were severely injured) at a six-mile-distant pond where a landing platform had been built. Here the patients were placed in other litters, carried to the beach, rowed in a rubber boat to a waiting Coast Guard plane and flown to the hospital.

This was typical of rescue operations of major proportions in which helicopters are concerned, with hundreds of personnel, Coast Guard, Army and Navy, besides civilians, participating and in which a network of communications covering thousands of miles is called into action.

Then there are the smaller-scale rescues in which the same immediate help is put at the service of single individuals, as in the recent case of a commercial fishing captain whose arm was nearly severed in a winch. A helicopter from the naval air station at Quonset Point, Rhode Island, picked him up and took him to the hospital at Wood's Hole, where the arm was saved. Such rescues are innumerable.

No job is too small or too large for the helicopter. One of the largest jobs was recently undertaken when the turbine-powered SH-3A was put into operation, the world's largest amphibian helicopter and the first one able both to search out and to destroy enemy submarines. Heretofore helicopters had performed only one of these functions during a single mission and still achieved maximum range. The SH-3A, being built by Sikorsky for the Navy, is the second turbocopter ever built with a boat hull, the first being the smaller S-62, powered by a single-engine gas turbine. This boat hull permits landing on and taking off from water, as well as from land, ice, snow, tundra, or swamp, since anti-submarine missions require long periods of overwater flight. The SH-3A features improved submarine-detection equipment and navigation system, and as one of the new generation of turbocopters it has of course increased payload, faster cruising speed, and great combat range. The rotor-blade anti-icing equipment gives it increased capability for 24-hour operation in any weather. It is, in fact, known as the Navy's first all-weather helicopter.

As typical of the swift course of change from piston-engine to turbine-engine power in helicopters, Sikorsky's experience may be cited. Its interest and research in helicopters powered by gas turbine go back to the 1940s, when its engineers first began considering the potential of such a machine. No concrete action was taken then, however, because at that time there were no gas-turbine engines suitable for rotary-wing aircraft. But in 1951 a Sikorsky proposal to the United States Army for a turbine-powered helicopter was accepted, and the company built the YH-18B, a modification of the S-52 type piston-engine helicopter, and powered by the Turbomeca Artouste II engine. Its first flight was in July, 1953.

Later came the HSS-1F, a modification of the S-58 type helicopter, the piston engine being replaced by two General Electric T-58 engines, and this was followed by the S-62, the first amphibious, boat-hull type. The SH-3A descends therefore from the now famous and hard-working S-58, the Navy's only anti-submarine helicopter until the SH-3A.

Among the other noteworthy helicopters of the moment, all of which are turbine-powered, is the Kaman

H-43B, powered by a Lycoming T-53 gas-turbine engine. This is the rescue helicopter nicknamed the "Huskie" by the Air Force, which has ordered it in quantity for crash-rescue work at air bases in this country and overseas—the first large order for helicopters the Air Force has ever made. The Huskie comes equipped with hoist, litter racks, and a specially designed fire-rescue kit. It was Kaman Aircraft Corporation, incidentally, which flew the world's first turbine helicopter in 1951 and the first twin turbine in 1954. And Bell has the HU-1 Iroquois, and the Model 204.

Also important, though from lack of space we mention them briefly, are the Lycoming T-53, the General Electric T-56, the Hughes 289, the Brantly B-2, and the Vertol 107, now in production. The Bell HV-1 is in a fine tradition: the Bell 47, one of the most famous helicopters ever built, was the first copter to receive a certificate of airworthiness from the Civil Aeronautics Administration.

Among my boyhood heroes was Leonardo da Vinci, a great artist, a skilled craftsman, an accomplished engineer, a noted architect and builder, a musician, a military expert, a teacher, an inventor. Nature had endowed him with more gifts than any other person of his period.

It is as an inventor I remember him best. Among his works that are still preserved is a series of detailed drawings showing a practical airplane and a helicopter, either of which could have flown had there been available an engine of suitable power and lightness. These brain children of da Vinci came into being about the time Columbus was preparing for his voyage to the Western Hemisphere.

Even as a lad I could visualize the possibility of horizontal flight for I had seen eagles, hawks, gulls and other birds move through the air in that way. But a machine that would rise vertically from the ground remained beyond my imagination until that memorable day in 1941 when Igor Sikorsky showed me the motion picture of his first helicopter in which he was at the controls.

Since that day I have seen many helicopters engaged in many activities. But in spite of all I now know about them, from da Vinci's dreams to Sikorsky's masterly execution and up to this moment of jet power, they still remain creatures of mystery and magic, able to move as they do forward, backward, and to either side.

CHAPTER SEVEN

Genesis of a jet

It was by the merest chance I caught a glimpse of what appeared to be a very small plane streaking at incredible speed across a patch of blue sky between two cloud masses. Not until some seconds after its disappearance did I hear the roar of its exhaust, a monstrous hurricane of noise unlike any I had ever heard. As the bellow rose in intensity and then diminished in gradual degrees, it left with me the impression of a sphere of sound rolling through space in fruitless pursuit of the fleeing plane. The rate at which jet aircraft—liners, bombers, fighters—has been developed in the ten years since then, and especially in the last three or four years, is just as amazing as the ever-increasing speed with which it flies.

During a 1949 flight in a DC-3 I asked one of the world's foremost aviation engineers for his opinion on the future of jet propulsion. His reply was prompt and graphic, "The jet in some form will power the plane of the future. In another decade or so reciprocating engines such as we have on this plane will be as outdated as the horse and buggy."

"What are the advantages of the jet engine, besides speed?" I asked.

"They are many," he replied. "First its simplicity. The turbo-jet engine has, comparatively, only a few moving parts—notably the turbine which is nothing more than a rotating fan of tremendous power. The engines used in today's commercial planes have literally hundreds of moving parts, all of them subject to constant wear that eventually means replacement or the scrap-pile. Weight is a most important factor. The jet engine weighs but a fraction of the reciprocating engine of similar power. Its simplicity greatly reduces maintenance costs. In an emergency it can be taken out of a plane and another put in its place in little more than an hour with tremendous saving in cost and labor."

The chief engineer paused a moment and then continued, "Now don't misunderstand me. The advantages of jet propulsion which I've mentioned are in a sense outweighed by some of its characteristics. It gobbles up fuel at an alarming rate, almost three times as fast as does the conventional engine. That means of course it must carry a proportionately heavy fuel load. Now much of our effort in aeronautical engineering is devoted to getting rid of weight, so you can see that the future of jet propulsion lies to a considerable extent in the hands of the chemist who, we hope, will give us a fuel of which one pound will deliver energy equal to that delivered by two or more pounds of the fuel being used today."

"Besides fuel-burning propensities, what other major problem does the jet engine present?" I inquired.

"Heat," he answered. "The blast of burning gases reaches a temperature of about two thousand degrees Fahrenheit which is considerably higher than the melting point of most metals. Here, too, the aeronautical engineer must await the result of the metallurgist's efforts in producing metals that will resist extraordinary temperatures and at the same time be available in an emergency."

"What fuel is generally used in the jet engine?"

"Just ordinary household kerosene has been found satisfactory but there is a catch even in that. The production of kerosene at the refineries falls short of even the requirements of the jet planes in use at present."

"Then what fuel is used to compensate for the shortage of kerosene?"

"High octane gasoline has been used with considerable success. But there, too, we have the obstacle of greatly increased cost. A ton of high octane or a ton of domestic kerosene makes a big difference in the cost of fueling a jet plane."

"Why is the kerosene supply so limited?" I asked.

"It is just a matter of evolution," he replied. "In our grandfathers' day whale oil was the common illuminant. After the modern petroleum industry began in the United States in 1859, the kerosene lamp replaced the whale oil lamp and kerosene cookstoves became popular with housewives. Later as gas and electricity dethroned the oil lamp and stove, the demand for kerosene diminished. Since hundreds of products now can be made from crude petroleum, the oil refineries convert it into fuel oil, gasoline, benzene, naphtha, ether and numerous drugs, dyes and even artificial rubber. Until recently the supply of kerosene was adequate for rural and isolated areas where the oil lamp and kerosene stove are still in use. But remember that a single jet plane will burn in a single hour enough kerosene to supply an average family for several years."

"What causes the jet plane to fly at such astonishing speeds?" I then asked.

The engineer hesitated a moment. "That is not so easy to answer," he said with an enigmatic smile. "Now if you were to ask me what gives the jet plane motion, I would ask you to think of yourself as standing with your back toward a wall. If you were to put a broom handle over your shoulder and press it back against the wall, your body would move forward. In other words the backward thrust of the broom handle is converted into the forward motion of your body. Basically it is the backward thrust of the column of gases against the atmosphere which gives the plane its forward motion. However, flying with the speed of sound at great altitudes where the air has little density is another matter. There are phenomena we do not quite understand but we are learning every day."

"How old is jet propulsion?" I asked in schoolboy fashion.

"It is as old as the world," he said. "Certain species of marine life have been jetting themselves from place to place for countless centuries."

Since that conversation in 1949 such great and steady progress has been made in fuel economy and in the creation of "super-alloys" for resisting oxidization at high temperatures that these problems, of which I then heard for the first time, are now well under control. In July, 1954, for instance, Pratt and Whitney Aircraft announced the development of a nickel-based, heat-resisting alloy for jet engine turbine blades; this "Waspaloy," named for the company's series of Wasp engines, permitted the engine to operate at higher turbine temperatures for longer periods of time.

Work on Waspaloy had started in 1949 with engineers seeking a metal to withstand the severe stresses encountered at temperatures of about 1,500 degrees F. When revolving at full speed, each turbine blade was subject to an outward pull equal to about 25,000 times its own weight, roughly equivalent to having eight average-sized automobiles hanging from the tip of each blade. The alloy had a base of more than fifty per cent nickel to which varying amounts of chromium, cobalt, molybdenum, titanium and aluminum were added.

That was only the beginning of a constant research and improvement, and the original Waspaloy, while still being used in certain stages of the Pratt and Whitney engines, has now been succeeded by increasingly efficient alloys in which newer metals, chiefly titanium, predominate.

Waspaloy, in its original form, was first used in blades for the company's J-48 engine, powering the Navy's Grumman F9F-5 Panthers and F9F-6 Cougars, and the Air Force's Lockheed F-94C starfires; while in its present development it is being used in their J-57 and J-75 engines, which power many of today's jet airliners, fighters, and bombers. As for fuel, or J.P.4, its military title, never-ceasing chemical research still goes on toward its perfecting.

It was at Grumman Aircraft Company at Bethpage, Long Island, that I first explored the mysteries which lie packed inside the sleek skin covering the slender body of the jet.

I was escorted to the "ready room" in which the jet pilots spent their time mostly in rest between test flights. Its comfortable leather-covered furniture and its appointments suggested a prosperous club. The pilots, young men in their physical and mental prime, took their ease as carefree as undergrads in a frat house. Within the hour some of them would be riding the winds, darting through space on a fiery broomstick. Yet neither in appearance nor manner did they slightly suggest the daredevil. Even their jovial camaraderie could not hide the deep-seated seriousness I had so often observed among men who live dangerously. Subject to rigorous medical examinations at frequent intervals, their physical and mental fitness was evident even to the casual observer. The cockpit of a jet is no place for a man with a toothache or a heartache, or anything at all on his mind except the immediate job. Every nerve and fiber of his body must be trigger quick if he is to land safely.

High above the ready room was the Tower, the nerve center of Operations. A house of glass, it was reached by way of a long spiral staircase. As I entered, the place somehow suggested the interior of a goldfish bowl. Its huge plate-glass windows gave an uninterrupted view of the flying field and its mile-long runway. The surrounding, flat countryside left exposed a vast expanse of sky. Below, on the huge concrete ramp, planes of several types suggested prehistoric monsters basking in the sun. Some were silent, some purred, others roared with a fury that was deafening.

At a desklike bench cluttered with instruments, a radio operator was conversing with distant pilots in a language scarcely a word of which I understood. Beside him sat an attractive girl wearing dark glasses because of the sun glare that filled the place. She, too, was a radio operator. As she spoke into the microphone before her, her soft voice had a pleasant quality, her diction was perfect, although her words meant nothing to me.

From outside on the ramp the low grumble of an idling jet signaled that a test flight was about to begin. Only the helmeted head of the pilot was visible under the plastic canopy.

Even from where I stood I could see him busy himself with several of the essentials preparatory to flight—straps to be adjusted on his ejector seat, his radio to be plugged in and tested, his oxygen to be checked, his controls tested. Since every movement of a piloted plane is directed from the tower, the pilot asked for radio check. "Coming in loud and clear," replied the radio operator beside me. "You are clear to taxi to Runway Thirty-three."

The grumbling increased to a snarling growl with the slight increase of power necessary for taxiing to the runway. The plane was one of the famous F9F Cougars, then favorites with the United States Navy as interceptors for use on carriers. Despite its name it more closely resembled an oversized shark warily nosing its way into strange surroundings. Fascinated I watched it taxi at a leisurely pace to the end of the runway nearly a mile distant. Turning its nose toward the Tower, it paused a moment or two like a sprinter on his mark. The pilot asked the Tower for "take-off clearance." The operator replied, "Flight number twenty-one cleared for take-off."

As the final word entered the microphone, the plane darted forward with rapidly increasing speed. For several moments it seemed to move in a mysterious silence, although I knew it was even then rending the heavens around it with the roar of a dozen tornadoes. Then I remembered that sound travels at about a thousand feet a second and the end of the runway was nearly five thousand feet distant.

The instant its landing wheels left the concrete and it was no longer earthbound, it seemed to enjoy its native element. It climbed up and up and up into the expanse of blue where there was not a cloud as big as its pilot's hand. It whooshed past the Tower and was gone in an instant, pursued by the rolling rumbling of a thousand locomotives simultaneously blowing off steam. Then came silence broken only by the ticking of a clock.

As my guide and I descended the spiral staircase, I felt as if I had witnessed a phenomenon as incongruous as a sunset in the eastern sky; a winged monster weighing several tons had streaked across my vision with no more visible means of propulsion than one would find on the Washington Monument.

The close-up view of a jet plane in full action stirred

within me an overwhelming desire to see the human and mechanical processes that entered the creation of such a complex and fearsome implement of national defense.

In the engineering department, large as a football field, complete concentration was evident on every face of the hundreds who worked at drafting boards or with slide rules or with strange devices beyond the ken of the layman. Here were born on paper the brain children of a corps of engineers, each a specialist in his particular part of the current project. "Engineering," as the department was called, was a place of hush, where of course many secrets were carefully guarded against prying eyes. A stranger there, no matter how well sponsored, was looked at, if not with actual suspicion, at least with a certain inquisitiveness. That was as it should be.

It was like stepping into another world when I was ushered into a vast workshop in which apparently no two jobs were alike. The place was a bedlam of sounds that at times had a symphonic quality of crescendos and diminuendos; arpeggios and pauses followed in quick succession as if some unseen baton were directing an opus titled "Industry." Filing, rasping, sawing, hammering, riveting and welding blended in a mighty chorus that somehow suggested Wagner. When I asked my guide what this strange craftshop was called, he answered, "File and Fit."

Here the brain children of Engineering were translated from blueprints to tangible prototypes of vital parts that would eventually take their place in the astounding procession of arts and skills that contributed to the production of the Cougar. I noticed that in this department the workers were seasoned craftsmen to whom a ten-thousandth of an inch was a mile-wide gap between success and failure. Their complete concentration on the varied objects on which they labored indicated clearly that they were proud of their workmanship. Here as in other departments I was conscious of the abstract beauty that is inherent in the functional design of hundreds of objects that would soon be copied in more substantial form and fitted into their appointed places in one of the world's most complex mechanisms. There was a strange similarity in the faces of the men who worked in File and Fit. The resemblance was not physical. Of many national origins and widely different ages, sizes and builds, they were at first glance such a group as one might see at a lodge meeting. On closer inspection, however, one discovered a certain intellectual quality in every face. In different garb or surroundings they might well have been taken for artists, sculptors, musicians or even professors.

It was with a feeling of regret that I left the department for an adjoining building and a complete change of pace and scene. The assembly of the F9F-8, familiarly known as the Cougar, was a sight never to be forgotten. Thousands of inert items joined together in mysterious wedlock that culminated in the completion of a winged creature of metal and fire that could outstrip the hurricane three to one, leaping into the stratosphere over thirty thousand feet in a matter of minutes. Ten miles a minute, six hundred miles an hour was its supreme speed in level flight.

As the door opened into the huge assembly department, a vast canopy of fluorescent lights made the place bright as a summer's day although there was not a window to be seen. The conditioned air was sweet and clean as a breeze on a mountaintop.

At first the scene was a confusion of strange shapes and forms among which men worked studiously rather than laboriously. The medley of sounds that marked File and Fit was absent. There was only the hum of activity incidental to assembling rather than fashioning the thousands of parts.

At the head of the assembly line that we were to follow through aisle after aisle, there stood what appeared to be a ponderous cylindrical casting from which protruded on either side what was obviously a rudimentary wing. It was the basic member around which the plane was to be built. A few steps further on was a similar cylinder, but here and there on its surfaces were adjusted a growing number of fittings and tubes and odd-looking gadgets the purpose of which only an engineer would know. At the next stop the cylinder had structural additions dotted with terminals and interlaced with a maze of varicolored wires and tubes and studded with clusters of amazing devices.

Swinging from an overhead crane, a massive assembly of metal cylinders teetered as it was lowered into place in an embryo plane. It was the engine, the source of the fiery blast that would breathe life into the three-ton monster.

When the engine was installed, miles of wiring and furlongs of hydraulic tubing would be added. At this stage the plane resembled an anatomical chart of the nervous, venous and arterial systems of a human being.

As wings and tail assembly were added, it was recognizable as a plane. In and around the tiny cockpit was installed a bewildering array of instruments and accessories, batteries, oxygen flasks, cooling apparatus, radio and the firing mechanism for the plane's four fifty-caliber guns.

The pilot's seat, as strange a contrivance as had ever come from the mind of man, was reminiscent somehow of a medieval torture device. It was known as the "pilot ejector seat" and its purpose was to catapult the pilot out of the cockpit should an emergency arise.

Having followed the evolution of the F9F-8 from its embryonic state to its ultimate completion, I was filled with wonder at every step. Here near the great door it stood waiting to be towed out on the ramp to join others of its kind ready for their initial test, miles above the earth. From its sharklike nose where its nostrils served as gun ports, to the barrel-like outlet for the flaming gases under its tail assembly, the device that fascinated me far more than any other was the ejector seat. Narrow-backed and made of metal, it was slightly higher than the seated pilot. At its top and immediately behind the flier's helmet, set into the frame of the seat, was what appeared to be a black rectangular head pad. Actually it contained a parachute that was not intended for the pilot but for the seat. The pilot was harnessed to his own chute on which he sat. Metal foot-rests protruded from the lower part of the seat, to be used only in an emergency. Attached vertically to the rear of the seat was a three-inch steel tube. It was really a gun barrel in the breach of which was a charge of gunpowder. Its firing mechanism was connected with two loops of nylon rope immediately above the pilot's helmet. In an emergency with the plane quite out of control, the pilot pulled a lever that set his complex lifesaving apparatus on a hair trigger, then he took an attitude in which his spine from head to pelvis was held rigidly vertical. He pulled the nylon loops and the protective curtain, to which they were attached, down over his face This action set off the explosive charge. Instantly several things happened, almost simultaneously. At the moment of explosion the canopy under which the pilot sat blew off, knee stirrups grasping his knees to prevent his legs from spreading. His radio earphones, transmitter, oxygen tubes and G-suit connector were automatically pulled from their connections. Pilot and seat, still strapped together, were shot fifty feet upward, escaping by a fraction of a second the knife-sharp tail of the plane. From the pad behind his head a parachute ballooned out and retarded slightly the rush to earth two or more miles below. With the seat-parachute in operation the pilot prepared for his leap to safety.

Undoing the belt and shoulder straps that bound him to the seat, he slipped gently into the empty air. Hurtling downward, he waited until gravity had put a safe distance between him and the pursuing seat. Only then did he pull his parachute release. Then suspended on a silken bubble, he floated earthward.

The complete story of engine design in any company would make many-volume reading. It would indeed be the technical inner story of all aviation. Let it only be said here that, in the case of Pratt and Whitney Aircraft, the company chosen for this book as representative, constant work goes on in refining the design of existing engines and in bringing out engines of new types. The most outstanding engines now are the J-57, the J-75, and the newer J-52 and JT-12, with increasing ability to produce high thrust when needed, and with outstanding fuel economy at cruise power conditions. The J-57 and J-75 are proven favorites with both Navy and Air Force, and the J-52, newer in the field, powers the Navy's A2F-1 Grumman attack plane.

With the JT-12, put into operation in 1960, Pratt and Whitney have moved into the small turbojet engine field. Until recently, all their engineering efforts have been in developing larger engines for the military, but the diminished emphasis on the use of large gas turbines, due to the military trend toward rockets and non-air-breathing engines, has enabled the company to turn to the development of a small engine. This JT-12, weighing only 430 pounds and producing 3,000 pounds of thrust, is applicable for installation on military-transport aircraft such as the Lockheed Jetstar, McDonnell UCX, and North American Sabreliner. And in addition, it can also be used in missiles and in helicopters.

There is also the new propeller-turbine engine, the T-34, which powers the C-133 transport, the first of the giant Douglas turboprop cargo planes to be completed for the Air Force.

Many flight records have been set by planes powered by Pratt and Whitney engines. On May 19, 1963 the Presidential VC-137 (Boeing 707-320 B) flew 5,004 miles nonstop from Washington, D.C., to Moscow at an average speed of 580 miles an hour. This plane was powered by four Pratt and Whitney JT-3D turbofan engines, each producing 18,000 pounds of thrust. The turbofan engine is a development of the turbojet engine. Its enlarged fan system takes in and discharges more air, producing more thrust at less fuel cost than the earlier types.

CHAPTER EIGHT

Flying on a flame

It was my good fortune to be well acquainted with Joseph Gaeta, who, as a test pilot during World War II, put the Navy's Hellcats and Wildcats through their paces while they were still fresh from the assembly line. It was he who introduced me to the workings of a jet and even helped compress me into a pilot's G-suit, at that time the last word in what the well-dressed airman should wear, but now, though still as hard-working as ever, being thrust out of the limelight by the new space suit.

As he led me out on the ramp where several Cougars seemed to be taking a breathing spell between flights, Test Pilot Gaeta remarked, "It's impossible to appreciate the engineering wonders in a jet and the hurricane of power stored up in it without actually sitting in the cockpit during a flight. As that is impossible, since the cockpit is barely large enough to hold one man, the pilot, I'll ask George to demonstrate to you on the ground."

George Davidson was a husky figure of a man on the sunny side of middle age. Although not a pilot, he knew his jets down to the last rivet. As assistant to the plant superintendent, he had a personal interest in every plane coming off the assembly line. He knew their whims and individual temperaments as a good trainer knows every thoroughbred in his stables.

Near us stood an F9F-8 quietly awaiting its first flight into the blue. It seemed to have shrunk in size. Indoors it towered over men and machines; in the open it was dwarfed by the huge bulk of the building in the background. Smooth from nose to tail, it might have been blown in glass, its canopy some eight feet above the ground. I became curious as to how the pilot could climb to his seat. A closer view revealed small semicircular openings in its side, one above the other; they were actually steps for the pilot's use.

A mechanic opened a tiny flap on the side of the plane; it concealed a switch that put in operation the hydraulic mechanism that slowly moved the canopy over the cockpit in a backward direction. Spry as a lad of one third his years, George clambered into the cockpit.

Meanwhile a truck on which was mounted a powerful electric generator, took its position behind the left wing. A heavy cable was led from it to the plane. Power sufficient to turn the turbine up to its required starting velocity was far greater than that supplied by the plane's battery. The portable dynamo developed six hundred to eight hundred amperes.

At a signal from George, now confined under the closed canopy, the man on the generator turned on the current and life throbbed within the plane. The turbine or rotor of the engine set up a low whine that gradually grew in volume as velocity increased. Engrossed with the instruments on the panel, George waved a restraining hand to the man at the generator and turned on the spark. There was a whoof and a whosh from the tail of the plane as the ignited gases stormed from the outlet with a thunderous growl over which the piercing note of the turbine blades set up a shrill scream.

As the throttle was opened, the invisible jet sounded off with a sustained roar so deafening that I could not hear the words shouted in my ear by Pilot Gaeta. As the throttle was closed, the storm of sound died down to the mere rumble of a cataract. George demonstrated the amazing articulation of the wings. Smoothly as the hands of a clock the flaps in the rear of the wings were lowered while the solid leading edges seemed to disengage themselves and incline downward until the cross-section wing structure seemed to take the form of a flat inverted U. Almost instantly two transverse sections of the belly of the plane opened slowly downward like a pair of large trap doors; they were brakes to retard the speed of the plane preparatory to landing or for any other imperative reason.

Then like a proud father showing off the accomplishments of his first-born, George smilingly pulled a lever here and pushed a switch there. The wing tips rose slowly and majestically high above us. The retraction of the wings is merely a space-saving device which enables a carrier to accommodate a large number of planes.

So dramatic is the jet plane in its design and construction as well as in its power and performance that one is likely to overlook the men who have mastered it in its breath-taking flight.

Cramped into a space so small that it is difficult to believe it would accommodate a full-grown man, the pilot sits surrounded by a bewildering array of dials, devices and controls, every one of which is vital to his safety and the safety and efficiency of the million-dollar plane he is flying.

Encumbered by a mass of equipment, free movement is almost impossible. When ready to fly, he is accoutered in crash helmet, large as a three-gallon pot, a Mae West life preserver and his protective G-suit that keeps his "innards" in place and his blood from rushing to his feet when pulling out of a power dive. From his helmet dangle wires connected with built-in earphones and transmitter. From his oxygen mask emerges a yard-long rubber hose and from his left side protrudes a cloth-covered tube known as the "G-suit connector."

Now all these appendages are connected with a device known to pilots as the "Elephant's Trunk." Add to these his safety belt and the shoulder straps that secure him to the ejector seat and you have a fairly good picture of a visitor from Mars about to take off for his native planet. Behind him and but an arm's length away his roaring engine belches two thousand Fahrenheit degrees of heat. From this he is more or less effectively protected. The heat generated by skin friction, however, as the plane hurtles through the air, is often insufferable in spite of the cooling system.

To all this physical impedimenta and discomfort is added a mental and nervous strain that is incessant from take-off to landing. At four or five hundred miles an hour there is little time for calculating position; he can get as lost as a blind man in the middle of the Sahara in just a minute or two. Normally of course he is aided by his radio but even the best of radios will fizzle out without warning.

The mere fact of getting lost is not the pilot's chief worry: It is his fuel supply that concerns him most. While the jet can cover great distances in a twinkling, its time in the air is limited by its fuel consumption of about five hundred gallons an hour. For this reason the pilot in difficulty thinks in terms of minutes rather than miles.

I was astonished to learn from jet pilots that the apparently smooth flight of a jet as observed from the ground, is a grand illusion. The pilot's specially devised helmet and the straps by which he is secured in his seat often save him from serious injury by being bounced around when he encounters turbulent air currents and cloud formations. The soft fleecy masses of vapor we see floating lazily in the sky become hard and unyielding. "Sometimes," said Victor Eble, one of the test pilots, "when you hit one of those clouds, it feels as if you had hit the roof of a building."

It was in the "ready room" I was introduced to the G-suit. At first glance it differs little in appearance from a suit of khaki-colored coveralls. On closer examination I discovered that in some places it contained several thicknesses and that the back was laced up like an old-fashioned corset. Attached to the left hip was a two-foot tube with a diameter of about an inch. At the end of the tube a bright metal connection only added to the mystery.

For many years the moment when the pilot pulled out of a power dive was the crucial one. As the plane changed its course from the almost vertical to level flight, the pilot often blacked out into total unconsciousness, a result of his blood being drawn from his brain by centrifugal force. This force or "pull" is measured in gravities or "Gs." In the language of the test pilot eight gravities mean that at the moment of directional change, the gravitational pull on the pilot is increased that number of times or in layman's language, his weight is increased eight times.

Every plane, regardless of its type, must undergo a series of test flights before it receives official approval as airworthy. In the case of military planes, power dives resulting in a specified number of Gs are often a requirement. In those early days the blackout of the pilot was considered a vocational hazard that was unavoidable. Casualties were frequent. Physicians, engineers, medical men and pilots joined in an effort to create a device that automatically would control the rush of blood from the pilot's head to his feet and brace his internal mechanisms against the violent shock of the pull-out.

After much experiment and testing by trial and error the sturdy G-suit emerged. It replaced the cumbersome body bandaging to which the pilot was subjected before a test flight. In normal flying it is a comfortable and practical garment. During the dangerous moments at the end of a dive, it seems to become a living thing, holding in its tight grip the torso and limbs of the wearer.

At this point Pilot Gaeta took from a locker a G-suit that was my approximate size, saying, "You've got to wear it and feel it if you really want to learn how it operates. Suppose you get into it. We'll help you."

Removing my street clothing, with the aid of the pilots I was soon encased in the G-suit. It felt a little bulky over my abdomen and around my thighs and tight under my knees. The feeling of rigidity over my spine was increased almost to the point of discomfort when the heavy corset-laces were pulled so tightly that my figure took on the lines of an hourglass. Gaeta picked up the tube dangling from my hip and placing the connective to his lips, blew into it with all his might. Instantly an air chamber over my abdomen inflated with such force, it was as if a mighty hand were pressing my stomach against my backbone. Simultaneously the air pressure seemed to grip my thighs with the power of a boa constrictor, the area under my knees was pinched tightly.

After the suit had been inflated several times, Gaeta remarked, "If you want to retard or stop the flow of a liquid through a rubber tube, you simply pinch the tube. This is exactly what the G-suit does. The pneumatic pads, inflated by the great air pressure at the end of a dive, press in on veins and arteries and so stop the downward flow of blood. The abdominal pad also gives support to the internal organs and keeps them in place despite the forces that would wrench them from where nature intended them to be."

But fashions change, and nothing is more indicative of the tremendous swoop upward which aviation has taken in the last three or four years, than the new space suit, or full-pressure suit, which I saw pictures of as I sat talking with a group of Air Force men the other day. It is the suit worn by the first man to pilot the X-15 into outer space, the young Sergeant told me proudly, and the Captain added, practically and with some understatement, that it is lighter and offers more protection than any previous suit worn by airmen. It is designed to hold at arm's length the extremes of both cold and heat. It is known as the MC-2 full-pressure suit. The look of it, as you may see in the reproduced photograph, is somewhat formidable. The wearer, it seems, will be fed in flight by a highly concentrated food squeezed out of something akin to a tube of tooth paste.

This is not a book about missiles, but North American's X-15, being a *manned* rocket, does come within our scope. This rocket ship with a cockpit, using a combination jet and rocket fuel, is a joint endeavor of the U.S. Air Force, the NASA (National Aeronautics and Space Administration), the Navy and North American Aviation, Inc., to produce a manned aerospace craft. In 1960 Major Robert White broke the world altitude record in the X-15, reaching beyond the atmosphere to a height of 136,000 feet from earth. The X-15 has already attained very high speeds and can exceed 4000 miles per hour. Unlike the cruder space trips of Gagarin and others, this is truly pilot-controlled space flight, a big step toward a manned satellite.

Air Force fighters of up-to-the-moment importance include the North American F-100 Supersabre, the McDonnell F-101 Voodoo; the Convair F-102 Delta Dagger, a long-range fighter; the Republic F-105 Thunderchief, the Western world's first all-weather fighter-bomber, scheduled for 1960 operation; and the Lockheed F-104 Starfighter, which holds the world's altitude record of 91,243 feet, using the General Electric J-79 engine. Its rate of climb, or "time to climb," is better than 50,000 feet per minute, which, as the Sergeant said, is "going straight up at about six hundred miles an hour." Someone else spoke of it as "getting upstairs on the double," for not the least intriguing thing about all this air activity is the new and casually vivid vocabulary it brings with it.

Notable among Air Force bombers are the Convair B-58 Hustler, the nation's first supersonic bomber, which carries a detachable "pod," enabling it to perform a greater variety of missions; the Boeing B-47 stratojet; and the famous Boeing B-52 long-range Stratofortress.

Among today's favorite Navy planes are the Douglas fighters Skyray, F4D and Skylancer, F5D; the Chance Vought fighters Crusader, F8U and the F8U-2; the Douglas attack bomber Skywarrior, A3D, all powered by the J-57; and, by the J-75, the Chance Vought fighter, F8U-3, and the Martin patrol plane Seamaster, P6M.

The names of jets now historic should also be on record. For instance, the Douglas Skyrocket of a few years ago, an experimental Navy craft whose jet engine was supplemented by rocket engines to attain its flight of 750 miles an hour. Also the North American F-86, a favorite of the Air Force, which held the world's official speed record of 670 miles an hour for jet planes.

And of course the Lockheed F-80, well known as the Shooting Star: in track parlance a sprinter that could cover comparatively short distances at incredible speed. It was a pygmy with room enough in its cockpit for one man provided he was not too large, and because of this dwarf size it could carry only the very limited amount of fuel that its giant appetite consumed in flight. For this reason the job it did in getting itself across the Atlantic was a surprise.

It was with some misgivings that, in the year 1948, many members of the Army Air Force learned of a proposed flight of a squadron of sixteen Shooting Stars from Michigan to the mid-shires of Britain. The jets, they reasoned, were designed and built solely for short and speedy interception flights. There was the question of fuel; a Shooting Star could carry so much and no more; just enough for about two hours in the air. The slightest error in navigation would take one of those fast flying planes so far off its course that its chance of survival was practically nil, for there are no landing strips in the Atlantic.

From hundreds of experienced pilots, sixteen were hand-picked to fly as many Shooting Stars to victory or oblivion. Fifty-six officers and enlisted men, all experts, were assigned to the flight as a kind of auxiliary force. Two C-54s and a C-47 were to be used as convoying transports. A Fying Fortress was fitted out as a rescue plane. A Super-Fort, flying as a kind of advance guard and as a weather ship, was to lead the Great Flight. Tons of spare parts and supplies for any contingency were assembled. Great quantities of kerosene fuel were transported to strategic spots along the route.

Those were days of mounting emotions and nervous strains. Lieutenant Colonel David Schilling in command of the jet squadron brooded over his pilots like a mother hen.

From Selfridge Field, Detroit, to Odiham, England is approximately thirty-five hundred miles. To make the flight possible, several landing fields and fueling stations, each within two hours' flight time from the other, must be available.

Taking off from Selfridge Field, the squadron made its

first stop at Bangor, Maine; distance 750 miles. From there a seven-hundred-mile hop took it to Goose Bay, Labrador. Seven hundred and seventy-six miles away lay Greenland; where seven hundred and forty-five miles of ocean was between them and Meeks Air Field in Iceland. Between Iceland and Stornoway in northern Scotland stretched 670 miles of as bleak an expanse of ocean as you will find on the globe.

But the men in the cockpits, flying at thirty thousand feet, saw none of it. Thousands of feet below was spread a carpet of clouds, dazzling white in the morning sun. The rest was easy, a short overland hop of 190 miles, less than half an hour's flight time, brought them to Prestwick, a mere hour and a half from Odiham, their destination. The distance flown was slightly more than five thousand miles. The officially recorded flying time was twelve hours and thirty minutes.

The flight, while spectacular, added little to the stature of the jet. It merely proved that the tiny planes could cover long distances in a series of comparatively short hops, a fact that was already well known. True, it was a masterpiece of planning, logistics and co-ordination that may prove useful in a possible future emergency.

When I discussed jet propulsion with many men in many places in the earlier days, the phrase "fuel load versus pay load" invariably came up and seemed, at that time, to be the only insurmountable barrier between the jet and any long-sustained flight, particularly in transoceanic journeys: certainly the Shooting Star had not solved it. Since then the barrier has gradually been broken down, and the story of fuel and refueling would make in itself a fascinating saga.

Since man first flew, the need for extending the range and increasing the load of military and commercial aircraft has been an ever-present problem. Now, with the prevalence of the jet engine—burning as much as 100 gallons of fuel per minute—this problem of attaining range with load has become more critical than ever. But aerial refueling has come to the rescue and proved to be the answer. Flight Refueling, Inc., is devoted exclusively to the development of techniques to achieve safe, speedy, all-weather transfer of fuel between aircraft in flight, and to the perfecting of related equipment. The "Probe and Drogue" refueling system, outstanding for its simplicity and automatic operation, is an exclusive Flight Refueling development.

This company was founded in 1949 as an American affiliate of Flight Refuelling, Ltd., which, with United States Air Force encouragement, had developed the basic Probe and Drogue refueling technique in England, a first application of which system enabled Col. David Schilling, USAF, to fly the North Atlantic nonstop in an F-84 jet fighter. With the outbreak of war in Korea, FRI was called upon by the USAF to install Probe and Drogue equipment in KB-29M tankers already equipped with Flight Refuelling's older looped-hose system. Over Korea, the Probe and Drogue system was first used in combat operations and, with probe-equipped tip tanks, an F-80 jet pilot by Lt. Col. Harry Doris flew the longest fighter mission on record—five widely scattered strikes during fourteen hours without landing.

Today, use of Probe and Drogue equipment is constantly being extended to new types of aircraft. USAF fighters and bombers equipped with the receiver Probe include the Lockheed F-80, Republic F-84, North American F-86, North American F-100 Supersabre, and McDonnell F-101 Voodoo, while the tankers include the Boeing KC-97 and, newest in the field, the Boeing KC-135 jet tanker, powered by four J-57s. It was lights used during the hour-long refueling of three Boeing B-47 bombers by a KC-97 that were mistaken for "mysterious lighted flying objects" in February, 1959, by pilot and passengers of a commercial airliner. The Air Force, investigating, found out the truth of the matter! Among the current Navy planes capable of flight refueling are the fighters, the Douglas A4-D, the Skyhawk, and the McDonnell F3H-2, the Demon, and the Grumman trainer, the F9F-8T.

This Probe and Drogue equipment consists of two basic parts—the hose reel unit in the tanker and the Probe in the receiver. When refueling is to take place, the tanker trails a length of hose ending in an automatic coupling with a funnel-shaped Drogue around it. The funnel, about thirty inches in diameter, serves the twofold purpose of stabilizing the flight of the hose and providing a sizable target for the Probe.

The needle-shaped Probe, attached to the nose, leading edge of the wing, or wing tip tank of the receiver aircraft, is flown into the Drogue at a slow relative speed, around 5-10 mph, and a fuel-tight coupling is automatically established. The fuel can then be transferred at a high rate of flow. To safeguard against turbulent air conditions a motor-driven fluid coupling with constant-tension characteristics governs the reeling in and out of the hose, allowing for variations of distance between receiver and tanker during the operation. Pilots say that no more skill is needed for this procedure than does routine formation flying; less skill, in fact, than a landing.

As with the jet engine itself, so with the jet-refueling system: it has its first experience in military aviation before being completely adapted to commercial. But civil aircraft refueling is included in the FRI's long-range plans, and its engineering staff stands ready to work with airframe manufacturers in all phases of design. An artist's sketch lies before me as I write: of a jet airliner being refueled above the weather by a jet tanker. Once airborne, a plane can safely fly at a gross weight fifteen per cent greater than its permissible take-off weight, which might mean that for very long flights the pay load could be tripled by departing with reduced fuel and filling tanks en route. Which is what very likely sooner or later may occur.

No predictions have been made as yet as to nuclear-powered aircraft engines, although Pratt and Whitney Aircraft is presently engaged in research and development work on such an engine, in a federally owned facility in Middletown, Connecticut, under a contract issued by the Atomic Energy Commission.

For prediction, in the whole matter of the aircraft engine, is not a matter of guesswork, second sight or wishful thinking, but is based on long study and a close knowledge of one's powerplant. This has been shown in an astonishing (to the layman) way by the five-year-interval predictions made by that great engine man, Frederick B. Rentschler, who founded Pratt and Whitney Aircraft in 1924 and who was, at the time of his death in April, 1956, Chairman of the Board of United Aircraft Corporation.

In 1951 Mr. Rentschler made a speech entitled "The Next Ten Years," and five years before that he had made a similar forecast for the postwar period of aircraft engine development when the jet engine, with the war over and more time available, could get a fuller concentration from the manufacturers. Someone said in 1951 of that earlier prediction, "His estimate requires no revision today," and now that almost all of "the next ten years" have gone by, the same remark might be made: no revisions are necessary to these forward looks based on a sure knowledge of what a plant can do and in how long, or how short, a time.

In the 1951 speech he first looked back to the 1946 forecast when "we believed that for the next five years at least, running to 1951, the world's commercial transports would be powered by piston engines. We stated further that very likely piston-engined transports would hold an important position on the world's airways for a subsequent five-year period, carrying to 1956.

"We also said that in the military program all new fighter planes during the 1946-1951 period would be built around jets, and that before the end of 1951 jet-powered medium bombers would be in production. Heavy bombers, in that same period, we judged, would continue to use piston engines. It was also our estimate then that heavy bombers powered by jets would be making their first appearance during the second five years, and would be going into production and service before the end of 1956." (We think here, of course, of the Boeing B-52, heavy, jet-powered bomber with more than 80,000 pounds of thrust available from its eight J-57 engines.)

"In commercial aviation," he said, "transports powered by piston engines will continue to be the workhorse of all the world's airlines through 1956. It is also our judgment that piston-engine-powered transports will continue in substantial operation up to 1961, at least."

And here, of course, we think of the jet-powered transports now about to come into service: the Douglas DC-8, ready for use at the end of 1959, and the Boeing 707, which has been in operation since January, 1959. Also, in reading what Mr. Rentschler had to say about propeller-turbine engines, we think of Lockheed's Electra, a turbo-prop airliner which began operation around the same time. He said:

"It is our own conclusion that no fleet replacement by American operators will occur until we know more about the relative transport merits of both the propeller-turbine and the jet. Early indications appear to favor the propeller-turbine not only for range and economy, factors of the greatest importance to successful airline operations, but because of its inherent operational characteristics. Three years at least will pass before we can know enough to make a sound decision. This, I think, means that there will be no start on fleet replacement until some time after five years. This conclusion is based both on the size of the transport contemplated, the life ahead of our present fleets, and the final proof and availability of the power-plants that will be needed."

The turboprop was third in the sequence of engines: piston, turbojet and turboprop; it utilizes, as its name implies, both propeller and jet engine, the exhaust gases of the jet engine being re-utilized to drive the propeller. This engine gives Hamilton Standard or any other propeller manufacturer a continuing outlet for propellers, even if the piston engine should entirely disappear, which it probably will not.

"It requires more than paper performance and experience for new powerplants and airframes to meet the exacting requirements of commercial transport service," said Mr. Rentschler in the fall of 1955 when Pan American Airways' purchase of forty-five Boeing and Douglas jet airliners marked the beginning of a new era in world transportation. "The experience of these past years, gained through heavy production and use for military requirements, has paved the way in this country to make possible safe commercial application of this new art.

"The real beginning of air transportation came only a little more than a generation ago. It followed five years of concentrated military development of the modern, radial, air-cooled engine. A pattern of sound development that brought America its aviation leadership was established in the early 1930s, which we have never relinquished.

"Even today, few realize that whether you come to the United States from Rome or Paris, London or Copenhagen, Manila or Tokyo, on foreign or U.S. airlines, you fly in American-designed and built airplanes powered by American engines."

H. M. Horner, who became chairman and chief executive officer of the United Aircraft Corporation after Mr. Rentschler's death, recently said of Mr. Rentschler and the great company he founded:

"I am aware . . . of Mr. Rentschler's old warning that, modern and advanced as we may think we are . . . still we only have scratched the surface. We have a host of military pilots today flying behind our jets who, at optimum altitude and speed, can fly faster than a bullet. Where we once thought a production engine producing 400 horsepower was the last word, pilots today are taking the equivalent of about 100,000 shaft horsepower from our J-75 and flying their production aircraft at speeds twice that of sound. If we think of the earth as surrounded by an envelope of air only 150,000 or so feet in height before it begins petering off into space and if we think not of the speed of sound but rather of the speed of light, Mr. Rentschler was indeed right. Astronomical speeds and distances lie ahead of us in the true meaning of astronomy.

"He was a man so capable of self-effacement that he was a myth even in his own lifetime. . . . Once he had seen an aircraft engine tick over and examined with his trained eye the scrupulous precision, for that time, with which the components were machined and finished, he knew his destiny. . . .

"Mr. Rentschler was a big man, rangy, powerful, and physically quick. But when he chose, he could sit motionless day after day, not daydreaming but thinking. When he stirred himself in the spring of 1925, he moved swiftly. Within a few weeks he organized Pratt & Whitney Aircraft as a completely private enterprise. . . .

"We have seen the airlines come, in little more than a

generation, from their real beginnings when they were quite a curiosity, to the point where now each day 140,000 men, women, and children use them on our domestic routes alone, and another 3,000 each day are aloft in them flying the Atlantic. Today children and grandmothers flit from coast to coast at cruise speeds of 359 miles an hour, and in the new jet transports at 550 to 600 miles an hour. I remember the time when our commercial air traffic for an entire year numbered only 5,000 hardy souls and I realize it was less than twenty years ago that Jimmy Doolittle suffered the arm cramp from holding the Wasp-powered Gee Bee racer at full throttle to set a new Thompson speed record of 252 miles an hour. . . ."

CHAPTER NINE

Airline in war and peace

Commercial air transportation, scarcely more than thirty-five years old, is now at the end of one era and the beginning of a new. The Douglas DC-7, cruising at 365 miles an hour, probably will be the last of the large commercial piston-engined air liners. Higher speeds are in demand, requiring horse power in excess of the reasonable capacity of the piston engine, and in the future it is expected that air transport will derive its greater powers from the turbine power-plant. The Jet Age is definitely here, in commercial as well as military aviation.

The growth of air transport has been so rapid that few realize its magnitude or its impact on our economy. To give an adequate picture of the present-day commercial sky traffic would demand several volumes. A profile of a representative airline will enable the reader to grasp more clearly the growth of the industry as a whole.

In January, 1930, several air transport companies were consolidated and became American Airways, Incorporated. Some had mail contracts, others had none. All were in more or less precarious financial condition. The historic depression was just getting into its stride. A total of

12,388 passengers was carried during that eventful year. In 1932 mail contract cancellations and unfavorable economic conditions brought about a reorganization of the company. American Airlines, Incorporated, was the result.

The new president, C. R. Smith, a dynamic personality who mixed daring with caution, began at once to introduce innovations. On seeing a "mock-up," wooden replica, of a Curtiss-Wright sleeping plane, he ordered several built and so, May, 1934, saw the first sleeper plane make a flight from Los Angeles to Dallas. It had few of the comforts and conveniences that were to be introduced later, when the Curtiss Condor, a cumbersome biplane, was added to the fleet.

With the Condor came the stewardesses who prepared meals, provided information and reassurance to timid passengers. During the ensuing two years the number of passengers doubled. The increase was attributed to the psychological effect of the stewardesses on many who hitherto had been afraid of flying.

Other innovations followed: first flight tests of Lorentz instrument landing, a system of airways' traffic control, preventive maintenance designed to keep the aircraft in operating condition at all times rather than allowing it to continue in service until repair or replacement was necessary. The Douglas DC-3 was built to specifications of American Airlines and was generally adopted by airline services all over the world. At President Smith's insistence the company engineers developed and tested the first direction-finder to be installed in a transport plane. Ultrahigh frequency radio for two-way communication between ground and plane and hydromatic full-feathering propellers were adopted in quick succession. The public soon caught the import of the numerous innovations that were to make air travel both safe and comfortable and that were adopted quickly by other airlines.

The chief problem of the air transport industry up to that period was persuading the public that in a plane there was no sensation of speed, or height, and that weather conditions only rarely interfered with schedules. Little by little public prejudice against air travel was broken down. Passenger travel increased at a startling rate, yet there still remained a large section of the population that refused to leave the ground while traveling.

Then came the 1938 hurricane that crippled all surface transportation along the Atlantic Coast. A few hours after the storm a number of American Airliners were en route to Boston. Thirty-three flights took place the day after the storm. During the following week the line carried seven thousand passengers between Boston and New York, nearly twice the number carried during 1927, America's first year of operation. The total of passengers reached an (until then) all-time high of 90,200 in 1938.

It is a curious fact that, despite the strides made in aircraft engineering, a successful windshield wiper for transport planes had not been developed until 1939. In that year American Airlines, after months of trial and error, installed in its planes a wiper that functioned so perfectly that it proved a major contribution to safety. In that year also American abandoned the practice of testing engines in flight; a new or overhauled engine got six hours of testing on the ground before it was installed in the plane. Equally important developments were being contributed by other companies to the general welfare of the industry that was even then suffering from growing pains.

Meantime American Airlines was enlarging its fleet to meet increased traffic and to compensate for the obsolescence of some of its older planes. Although dividends were still in the dim future, American continued, sometimes at great expense, to remove or at least minimize the few hazards that disturbed potential air travelers.

Planes in flight were now becoming numerous. In spite of stringent regulations that confined them to specified courses at predetermined altitudes, the hours of darkness brought anxious moments particularly in the areas of approach to airports. The possibility of collision could not be dismissed until American developed the first successful blinking navigation lights now required on all transport planes.

Came Pearl Harbor and chaos. Almost before the smoke of catastrophe had cleared away, American had turned over to the United States Army thirty-eight of its eighty-four twin-engined Flagships. In June, 1942, all airlines, including American, received a rush call from Washington ordering every available transport plane then in military service to land at the nearest airport, refuel and make a beeline for Edmonton, Alberta. The Jap fleet was heading for Alaska and a foothold on the American continent.

At first the task seemed impossible but American grit and resourcefulness swept aside all obstacles. Planes were stripped of their luxuries and converted into flying boxcars. Ammunition, medicine, food, machinery parts, barrels of gasoline and oil, lumber and nails and supplies for the Alcan Highway then under construction were loaded with feverish haste. Troops with battle equipment were packed in like sardines. Lonely Arctic outposts must be defended. Topographical maps, made by the Army in a preceding and well-timed global survey, were studied by the cream of the country's civil pilots.

In faraway Alberta a fabulous base sprang up as if by magic. Crews of skilled mechanics from American and other airlines kept the planes flying and civilian pilots, unaccustomed to the rigors of the subarctic, flew them.

From a modification center at LaGuardia Airport ninety-nine planes were conditioned to meet military requirements by the engineering and maintenance depart-ments of American. After vigorous test flights they were sent directly into combat service.

Although engaged in all-out war effort and still keeping its civilian transport in operation, American sent a five-man crew to blaze a trail across the South Atlantic to India, and the following year dispatched another crew on another exploration flight from Newfoundland to Marrakesh, French Morocco.

In American Airlines, as in other airlines, the business of war held priority. In executive offices and drafting rooms, laboratories and shops all-out effort was put forth to hasten victory. Conversion of sea water into drinking water for our Navy. Successful experimentation in pressurizing the B-29's cabin. Engineering, fabricating and installing radar equipment in the British B-24. This installation, the first of its kind, was adopted as standard procedure in allied planes. In the air as well as on the ground, the air transport companies did their bit. American Airline crews made 1,075 flights over the Burma Road of the Air, carrying more than five million pounds of bombs and gasoline for China.

With an eye on the restoration of peace and as a contribution to the war effort, the company established the Air Education Research in schools and colleges and began a personnel-training program for the American Air Transport Command. Pilots, mechanics, navigators, radio operators, control officers, priority officers and transportation officers were trained in schools in New York, Chicago and Burbank. Six DC-3s and two Lockheed C-60s were assigned for training.

As war's end drew nearer, the airlines began to prepare for the business of peace. In July, 1945, American Airlines and American Export Airlines were combined to form the first transocean airline system of its kind in the world. It was christened American Overseas Airways. The combination provided a one-system service by air from the North American continent to the British Isles and the European continent. The American Export Airlines had been operating as a transocean carrier since 1942 in commercial service and as a contract carrier for the Army Air Transport Command, also for the Naval Air Transport Service. It had gathered invaluable experience with four-engine planes in nearly eight thousand overocean flights.

By the end of the war American had built an organization of 11,450 trained persons. As in all branches of aviation, training of personnel continued to be of first importance. American opened two training schools, one at Tulsa, Oklahoma, for stewardesses and passenger agents, the other at Ardmore, Oklahoma, in the former Army Air base.

In March, 1948, the Ardmore Training Center had four thousand students, including pilots, flight engineers, stewardesses, mechanics, ticket and cargo agents and dispatchers. One hundred and ninety-five of the pilots were from other domestic and foreign airlines. More than eighteen thousand hours and 3,620,000 persons were flown in training flights without injury to a single student.

When the training center at Ardmore had fulfilled its mission, training of all male personnel reverted to individual stations and stewardesses (now called hostesses) were trained in a school at the Chicago Municipal Airport.

The standard set for the selection of airline hostesses is high. The minimum educational requirement is a high school diploma besides some business training; or two years of college with at least one year of business experience; or registered nurse certificate; or a college degree. A hostess must be between the ages of twenty-one and twenty-eight and have an attractive appearance: clear complexion, good teeth, good enough eyesight not to need glasses, be between five feet two and five feet seven inches tall and weigh no more than 125 pounds. She must have good judgment, a stable temperament and good character.

The required course of study includes theory of flight, meteorology, technical details of company planes, routes of all airlines, airline and flight terminology, governmental aeronautical organizations, navigation, flight control, ticketing and reservations, passenger service and food service.

American Airlines had, as we see, undertaken its first major expansion before the war ended. In 1944 the company had set up its Airfreight Division and introduced the first scheduled Airfreight Service. In 1945, the first full year of operation, Airfreight tonnages were negligible, but in 1953, less than ten years later, they had increased to 54 million ton miles, more than 2,800 per cent over 1945. For the year 1958 the amount was over 94 million ton miles, and still soaring.

The second major expansion in the immediate postwar years came in the size and composition of American's fleet; the company had ordered, in 1945, a completely new fleet of postwar passenger planes, consisting of fifty-four four-engined Douglas DC-6s and seventy-five twin-engine Convair 240s. The DC-3, once the ideal airplane, was no longer economical to operate. What was needed were faster and bigger planes to carry more people farther and in less time. These new craft were built to the company's specifications. Flying at three hundred miles an hour, they were pressurized to fly at high altitudes. The Convair seated forty passengers, about twice the number that the DC-3 would hold. The DC-6 Flagship seated fifty-two passengers. "Flagship," by the way, was the name born with the DC-3. Also, though size, range, and speed increased with the DC-6 and later the DC-7, the streamlining of air surfaces has remained essentially unchanged from that of the DC-3. With that aircraft, the slender and efficient lines of the modern transport were fixed.

By 1948, with these new aircraft appearing on its line, American had come through the second stage of its growth, the period of incipient maturity in which it carried passengers as well as mail, expanded its fleet and its route mileage, and reduced its subsidy costs. Now began the period in which service could be carried on without subsidy and at a profit. The last of the DC-4s, used to bridge the gap between the DC-3 and the new fleet, was taken out of passenger service on the last day of 1948, though used for a while for airfreight. The last of the DC-3s was retired on March 31, 1949.

The size and speed of the postwar planes presented the problem of airport expansion, for there were few airfields in the country that could match the new aircraft. Even before the end of World War II a program of airport expansion had begun, but the immediate need was for a braking device that could slow down the big planes on the existing, relatively short runways. In 1947 American met this problem by equipping its Flagships with reversible propellers, which within a few months other airlines were also using.

The first scheduled transcontinental low-fare air tourist service between New York and Los Angeles was inaugurated by American in 1949, using DC-6s converted to carry up to eighty passengers. In 1951 the company ordered seventeen Douglas DC-6Bs and eight more DC-6A Airfreighters. Also, in that year, the first DC-7s were put on order, final delivery being made in 1954. But it was in the previous year that American introduced, on November 29, 1953, the nonstop transcontinental DC-7, making the 2,500-mile New York-Los Angeles trip in less than eight hours.

A demonstration of what air transportation had become,

an index of its growth and of its importance to the national economy and defense, was made during the Korean War, which found American and other airlines prepared as they had not been in Pearl Harbor days, nearly ten years before. Forty per cent of the airlines' long-range planes were contributed to the Military Air Transport Service and between the start of hostilities in 1950 and the truce in 1953 the Pacific Airlift made more than 10,000 trips around the world. Enough high-priority personnel was carried to man some twenty reinforced infantry divisions, and cargo comparable to ten times all the 105 millimeter howitzers of all the infantry divisions in World War II.

Thirty years in existence, American Airlines had at the end of 1958 about 21,000 employees. Not only was there now not a trace of subsidy in its operating income but, in 1953, by carrying more than three billion passenger miles, it became the world's largest single carrier in terms of passenger revenue. In 1958 that figure rose to over five billion, and is now still higher.

Now as to the future: Although air transportation is over the threshold of the Jet Age, a large part of transport will for some time of course be powered by the piston engine, as evidenced by such advances as the airborne radar with which American has now equipped its fleet of long-range DC-7s. This is technically known as C-Band Radar, a Radio Corporation of America product. The "radome" in the nose has added some fourteen inches to the overall length of the plane, but the new pointed nose gives a more streamlined appearance. Bullet-shaped propeller spinners were added at the same time.

This radar equipment, or "eye," sends out a pulse which can be directed either up or down, or straight ahead up to a distance of about 150 miles. The pulse passes through nonturbulent weather but bounces back from turbulent objects such as heavy rain or snow, creating an image or "echo" on the radarscope. Anything which shows a marked change in the terrain, as river or coastline, also registers. There are two radarscopes in the cockpit, one each in front of the captain and the first officer.

Turbo-jet commercial aircraft domestic operation began when, on January 25, 1959, American Airlines put into effect the first transcontinental service for daily operation with the 106-passenger Boeing Turbo-jet, America's 707 Jet Flagship, powered by four Pratt and Whitney J-57 turbo engines. The Douglas DC-8, which went into operation with Pan American in 1960, is currently powered with a J-57, but later models have its sister engine, the J-75. These two engines will power 90 per cent of the Boeing and Douglas jet transports now going into operation.

In a transcontinental test flight made October 16, 1955, by the Boeing 707, the time of the giant jet airliner from Seattle to Washington, D.C. was three hours, fifty-eight minutes, averaging 592 miles an hour. The return flight, made the same day, took four hours, eight minutes, averaging 570 miles an hour. Present schedules for the 707 Jet Flagships are: Eastbound, Los Angeles to New York, four hours and thirty minutes; Los Angeles to Chicago, three hours and thirty minutes; Chicago to New York, one hour and thirty minutes; Westbound, New York to Los Angeles, five hours and thirty minutes; Chicago to Los Angeles, three hours and forty-five minutes; New York to Chicago, one hour and fifty-five minutes. Since 1959 the turbo-jet service has been extended to other cities on the American system.

Two new devices for the commercial operation of turbo-jet aircraft were provided by Boeing: a sound suppressor and an air brake. The suppressor is permanently fixed to the exhaust system of each engine, to reduce the noise commonly attributed to engines of the turbo-jet type. The

air brake gives thrust in a reverse direction and braking
ability on the ground similar in effect to that provided on
the conventional airplane by propellers which can be reversed when the aircraft is on the ground.

Also, the first turbine-propeller-powered transport to be
produced in the United States, the Electra from Lockheed
Aircraft Corporation, began operation on the routes of
American in January, 1959. This four-engined turboprop
is the joint work of engineers and economists for American Airlines and Lockheed. Its cruising speed is in excess
of 400 miles an hour, one of the fastest turbo-prop commercial airliners in service. The Electra is of completely
original design. Although a medium-size transport, it has
a cruising range of 2,000 miles. It has 8,000 feet cabin
pressure at a cruising altitude of 30,000 feet, and this type
of power provides higher cruising speeds over a wider
range of altitudes, from 5,000 to 30,000 feet.

The Electra is one of the most comfortable transports
built. A quiet cabin and a greater sensation of smoothness
are insured by the engine's special qualities and by new
techniques of soundproofing. The built-in loading steps
reduce delay by doing away with the need for roll-up loading ramps. Passengers are able to carry their luggage aboard
with them if they like, although provision has also been
made for checking it before boarding. (Four thousand
pounds of airfreight, express and mail can, incidentally,
be carried.) As for the interior, it is designed to reach a
new high in luxury and ease: it seats sixty-eight, with a
lounge for six; the seats are wider than any in airline use,
and each passenger has his own individual table and a
bigger view than ever before, from windows twenty inches
high and sixteen inches wide.

For those who appreciate architectural detail as well as
an easy trip, it may be added that the Electra has a wing
span of ninety-five feet, a fuselage 101 feet, four inches

long, and an overall height, to the top of the tail, of thirty-four feet. Weather-avoidance radar is of course standard equipment, as is automatic pilot, and control systems are of the aeronautically boosted mechanical type. Its reversing propellers insure ground control and its take-off and landing features are such that it can operate without difficulty from airports of approximately 5,000 feet.

Besides these, American's line include DC-7s, DC-6s and 6Bs, Convairs, and DC-6A airfreighters.

As an official of the company said the other day, in speaking of the present status and plans of the company: "American has not arrived at this point easily, or without disappointments. The company has put a good many problems behind it, and tomorrow, with every advance made, there will be new problems. American will meet them, confident of their solution. The economy of this country has come to depend on air mail, air cargo, air passenger service—and that dependence has created new traffic and travel and will continue to do so."

CHAPTER TEN

Aviation goes to school

During a recent interview an executive prominent in the aviation industry said to me, "In no other business do things change so quickly and so radically as in aviation. Every day brings new problems to be solved, new theories to be proved, new materials to be tested, new techniques to be tried. The innovation of yesterday becomes obsolescent tomorrow, and so it goes with every art and craft and skill entering the design, construction and ultimate operation of a modern plane. It is this constant advance that keeps every person engaged in the industry on his or her toes. In no other commercial field will you find such an extensive program of study and instruction or such rapid advance of those who have the God-given gift of learning quickly and thoroughly. Don't forget that the rapid growth of aviation has been due more to the development of men than to the development of machines.

"The engine in the Wright brothers' plane, the wings that supported it and the propellers that gave it motion were basically the same as those of the Stratocruiser, the Constellation or the DC-7 of today. Never has an industry vibrated with life and the energy of youth as does aviation and conversely, never have gray hairs and experience been so highly valued."

"How do you account for the glamour that aviation holds for the youth of America?" I asked.

"Youth attracts youth," he replied. "Aviation is young. Even at this moment it has scarcely reached maturity. It is still filled with dreams and visions of an adventurous future. Unlike most adult industries, it is still more concerned with its progress than with its profits. Its books prove this. It is this crispness of youth and freedom from dry rot in aviation that attracts young men and young women to all phases of the industry."

"Young women?" I queried.

"Yes," he said, "there are tens of thousands of bright girls who have been carefully chosen for many jobs in which intelligence, personality and a goodly store of common sense are essentials. These qualifications have been encouraged or stimulated by intensive instruction. Whether their jobs be in factory or office, in air terminal or laboratory, in the air or at a typewriter, you will find them imbued with the vibrant spirit of aviation and bubbling with pride in their work.

"In the early days when aviation was a sport rather than a business and pilots flew for pleasure rather than for profit, many of the outstanding fliers and even record holders were women. In whatever phase of aviation, on the ground or aloft, in which women have engaged, they, too, have demonstrated that an ounce of brain has been worth a pound of brawn in the development of the industry."

"What has aviation to offer a young man about to graduate from high school?" I inquired.

The executive pondered a moment before replying. "A high school or college diploma is not a passport to success either in aviation or in any other industry. It simply certifies that the holder has complied with certain academic requirements. It is not an index of his character, his industry or his ability to think clearly. On the other hand it indicates to the employer that an applicant for a job has received certain basic instruction that will enable him to profit by the specialized training that follows employment. In no other major industry is training in one form or another so essential or so continuous as in aviation."

"Can you explain why such unusual emphasis is placed on training?"

"Certainly," he answered. "In this plant seven thousand employees are engaged in more than a hundred jobs of which no two are like. They range all the way from engineering to unskilled labor. Now, eliminating the latter class, the others are working in designing, assembling and testing one of the most complex of modern machines. It must function with the precision of a fine watch. A moment of carelessness on the part of a single worker will nullify the work of the others, no matter how expertly it may have been done. In no other industry is teamwork so important or continuous instruction so vital."

"What is your advice to young people who see a career in aviation?" I asked.

"To those who are serious about it," he said quickly, "I recommend renewed effort in their studies, particularly in English, math, physics and chemistry."

"English?" I queried.

"Yes," he replied. "Where verbal orders or reports are given and received with frequency, slang or jargon or careless speech habits often fail to reveal the true meaning of the message. The result is confusion, misunderstanding and costly mistakes."

"Assuming that a young man without a high school or

college diploma wants to enter aviation, what should he do?"

"Many such young men are employed in the various branches of aviation," he said. "They start as unskilled labor. From the first day of their employment their progress lies in their own hands. The more ambitious go to night school or take correspondence courses on the subjects in which they are deficient. Others who have a natural knack of learning quickly while on the actual job, often make rapid progress. Those who merely live from payday to payday with little thought of the future, gradually drift toward the scrap pile."

"What is your opinion about aviation schools?" I asked.

The executive gave thoughtful pause to his answer. "A few are good," he said. "Others are fair. The rest are worthless since they are in business for profit with only a slight regard for the future welfare of their students."

"How can a prospective student determine which schools are good and which are not?"

"There are several ways. The Civil Aeronautics Authority, Washington, D.C., will send, on request, a list of government-approved schools. The Aeronautical Chamber of Commerce, New York City, will also assist a prospective student in choosing a school that will suit his requirements. In either case I would advise the student to find out the names and addresses of several graduates of the school he is considering. A short note asking their opinion of the school will bring reliable information. The better schools of course are as ethical in their dealings with students as are universities and colleges. A visit to one of the better schools would be a revealing experience.

"I speak now only of the engineering and mechanical aviation schools. So-called 'flying schools' of which there are hundreds, are another story. With a few exceptions they merely give a pupil elementary instruction in flying small planes. While the ability to take off, fly and land a Piper Cub in good style is a pleasant accomplishment, it is but little help to the student with limited funds who has his heart set on becoming a professional pilot. 'Flying hours' are an expensive luxury that only those with a healthy bank roll can afford. To turn out a proficient pilot costs the Army Air Corps in the neighborhood of seventy thousand dollars."

"But," I interrupted, "how did the thousands of professional pilots who are flying today get their training?"

"You will find," he answered, "that many of the more experienced pilots grew up with the industry. They began their flying careers when planes were comparatively simple affairs. Aviation was then only a budding industry unhampered by rigorous laws and regulations. Airways and airports were rudimentary, traffic was light and schedules were elastic. Flying skill rather than accumulated knowledge was the pilot's chief asset.

"Take the DC-3 of about twenty years ago, best plane of its period and the universal favorite of the world's airlines. Although costing about a hundred thousand dollars, it was as docile and as easy to handle as the family car. The operational and maintenance handbook used by pilots and ground crew was no larger than a modest telephone directory. When compared with the present-day DC-7, it was as a dollar watch is to a fine chronometer. The set of instructions that comes with the latter plane occupies ten volumes, each as thick as a Sears Roebuck catalog. The pilot flying one of those transports has in his hands a piece of property that may have cost his employers one million and a half dollars.

"It is obvious that to be trusted with the safety of such an astonishingly complex machine, to say nothing of its priceless human cargo, the pilot must have had long experience and endless training. In short, the gap between the student in a flying school and the pilot of a modern transport plane is as broad as that between a student of first aid and a distinguished surgeon."

"Do airlines employ former military fliers as pilots?" I inquired.

"Many excellent transport pilots have had experience in military flying," he replied. "However, it sometimes happens that the indoctrination, training and the philosophy of the military pilot unfit him for civil transport work. In military flying the Objective is paramount, even if it entail great risks. In combat the pilot, the plane and all in it may be, under certain circumstances, expendable. Caution may be a liability while daring to the point of recklessness has sometimes placed a pilot's name among the immortals of military aviation.

"In civilian transport flying safety takes precedence over all else. There is no room for heroics in the cockpit. Taking chances is prohibited. Even a suggestion of recklessness is a short cut to dismissal. In brief, civil air transport is a practical business in which safety must come first if there are to be profits later. This doctrine of safety permeates every nook and cranny of the entire structure of civil aviation. The man in overalls who works in maintenance is as deeply imbued with it as is the man in natty uniform who sits at the controls. Furthermore there are stringent laws to insure adherence to every safety standard that has been set up.

"I have dwelt on the airlines' adherence to safety at all costs, to emphasize the necessity of unremitting training of personnel regardless of the branch of aviation in which they may be employed. To absorb that training, however, those being instructed must have a certain backlog of knowledge, and that is where the schools come in, whether they be company schools or commercial enterprises known generally as 'aviation schools.' In our own plants for instance, we have found that those who have had pre-employment training make more rapid and better progress. Indeed, many of our most valuable employees hold diplomas from some of the better schools."

"What are the essentials of a good aviation school?"

"There are several," he said. "First there is good reputation, or integrity if you will. Secondly, a sound financial and business background. Thirdly, the number and standing of its graduates in the industry."

"Why do you consider a school's financial condition?" I inquired.

"Because equipment, materials, the faculty and general overhead demand large investment and sound business management."

"If I had a son who decided to take up aviation as a career, could you recommend such a school?" I asked.

The executive replied unhesitatingly, "There are several, any one of which would be a safe bet. Perhaps the more typical of the better schools would be the Academy of Aeronautics at LaGuardia Airport, New York. I consider Lee Warrender, the executive vice president, one of the best informed men in the world of aviation. A skilled pilot in the early days of the industry, he has come up through every branch of it and learned its rudiments and development by sweat and study. You should drop in and talk with him."

Again I journeyed to LaGuardia Airport and again I was thrilled by the dynamic scene. Hundreds of visitors lined the elevated observation promenade. Planes arriving, departing, taxiing and warming-up filled the air with the rumbling and roaring of motors. Passengers were entering or alighting from planes. There were crews whose stint in the air had been completed. Porters and baggage men, fuel trucks, towing trucks and baggage-laden hand trucks were scattered in orderly confusion. Nearby a building of modern design stood aloof from the hurly-burly that goes on day and night. It was the Academy of Aeronautics.

It would be difficult to imagine a more appropriate location for a school in which the objective of every student was employment in the aviation industry. Here was the constant stimulus of round-the-clock activities in one of the world's greatest airports. Even as I parked my car, several transport planes, gliding in for a landing, seemed so close to the roof of the academy as to enable one to touch their landing gear with a fishing pole. Because of their proximity to the runways, the Civil Aeronautics Administration limited the height of the academy buildings to two stories without projecting chimneys or other obstructions.

As I entered, I could hear the familiar buzz of industry I had heard many times before in the plants I had visited. While I chatted with Mr. Warrender, I was deeply impressed by his encyclopedic knowledge of aviation and its kindred industries. The members of the faculty to whom he introduced me and to whom I listened during classes had a simple directness in approaching their subjects. They used no fancy phrases nor did they expound vague theories. Their lectures were down-to-earth expositions of pertinent facts that would sooner or later be useful to young men impatient to be off about the business of life.

The students showed an eagerness and attention rarely seen even in the classrooms of the best universities. They made voluminous notes which were to be kept for future reference.

Visiting the Design department, I found myself in a huge glass-enclosed room in which more than a hundred students were at work over their drafting tables. T-squares, slide rules, drawing instruments were in evidence everywhere. Only the rumble and roar of planes on ramps and runways outside broke the silence that indicated complete concentration on the work at hand.

In an adjoining office the chairman of the Design department proudly spread out on the table several projects which had just been completed by students. It hardly seemed possible that these young men could master the problems and complexities of aircraft technology. On close examination, the drawings disclosed not only a broad grasp of design and construction but also an accuracy and flawless execution of which many a graduate engineer might well be proud.

"What are the entrance requirements?" I asked the chairman.

"The applicant must be at least seventeen years old," he said. "He must be of good character, a graduate of a secondary school and must present evidence of having completed a minimum of sixteen preparatory course credits. He must also have four units in English, one unit in elementary algebra, one unit in plane geometry and one unit in physical science. He is required to pass an entrance examination.

"These entrance requirements are the same for all three courses. At present, the Academy has three programs in the Day Division and three programs in the Evening Division: Aerospace Design Technology deals with the design and development of new aircraft and spacecraft; Aerospace Electronics Technology covers the development of new electronics equipment for the aerospace and related industries; and Aerospace Maintenance Technology deals with the manufacture, maintenance and overhaul of the aircraft, the powerplant and accessory systems. The evening school courses cover the same areas. These courses cover virtually every aspect of Aviation/Aerospace technology as we know it today.

"Every student, regardless of the course he selects, must follow the same basic program for the first two semesters. Drafting, mathematics, physics, English, materials and basic aircraft theories are included.

"Upon starting the third semester, the student enters his major area. The Design student follows a schedule of engineering-related subjects such as stress analysis, structures, aircraft design techniques and aerodynamics. He will design an original airplane before graduation.

"The Electronics student spends many hours in the laboratory performing a large number of experiments in electronic circuitry, microwaves, radar, transistor circuitry, servomechanisms, and telemetry. His goal is research and development rather than operation and trouble shooting.

"The Maintenance student enters the fascinating world of jets, electrical systems, hydraulics, control systems and operations and testing. Throughout his three semesters in the laboratory he will learn overhaul, operation and servicing. In addition to airline and general aviation maintenance procedures, he is qualified for many positions in aircraft manufacturing in the laboratory and on the flight line. He is qualified to write the test for the Airframe and Powerplant Certificate granted by the Federal Aviation Agency."

"An exciting curriculum!" I said. "What occurs if a student finds himself unable or unwilling to keep pace with it?"

"Our job is to advise as well as instruct," he answered. "If a student is unable to make the grade, we invite him for a friendly private chat during which we advise him to seek a more compatible and less exacting industry or trade."

"How do you account for the unusual concentration they show on their work?"

"The students have selected their courses of study with care, they have a profound interest in their subjects, and they have been thoroughly briefed on the need for a high degree of personal competence and integrity. Since the Academy is a private institution of higher education, every student is paying tuition and wants to obtain the most from his educational experiences."

The atmosphere throughout the many laboratories is one of planned accomplishment. In the Electronics laboratories students concentrate on the analysis of circuits, using the latest of measuring devices. Others are engaged in studying radar operation; still more are involved in a demonstration of servomechanism devices similar to those found on the latest aircraft and spacecraft.

In the basic drafting room, freshmen students concentrate on developing the techniques of the draftsman or confer with instructors about their progress.

In the powerplant test laboratory advanced students analyze engine operation, some on piston engines, others on the jet powerplant.

In the maintenance hangar senior students go about the business of aircraft overhaul and inspection. Students are assigned to multi-engined and helicopter aircraft to learn the routines of safety that are never really a routine but a carefully laid out plan to assure maximum safety in flight.

In the airplane laboratory, students work on the many systems that are an integral part of today's modern, high performance airlines—hydraulic systems, electrical circuits, specially designed air conditioning and pressurization systems, and instrumentation.

In the machine laboratory the students become familiar with the capabilities and limitations of machine tools, metal forming methods and the techniques of manufacturing.

For those working on the more advanced problems of design, the wind tunnel in which accurate models are "flown" and their behavior observed, holds a strong fascination. On the faces of the students I saw boyish enthusiasm blended with complete concentration. Their strange jargon, copious notes and symbols gave proof that despite the fun of flying a miniature plane in a miniature hurricane, they were serious men engaged in a serious job.

As I moved from department to department, from classroom to classroom, I was astonished by the diversity of the huge assembly of equipment used in preparing young men for their places in the industry.

The extensive laboratory equipment includes non-destructive testing equipment such as X-ray, zyglo and magnetic processes. In the materials laboratory, tensile testing equipment and heat treatment is in daily operation.

As the Academy developed into its present status of a technical institute, these laboratories were created to provide the knowledge and experience vital to the successful technician. They reflect with great accuracy the transistion that has taken place in the industry as it moved from aviation to aerospace in the past ten years.

Since I had covered the story of jet propulsion, I was fascinated by an Allison jet engine, a quarter section of which had been cut away for instruction purposes. I must confess that in the fifteen minutes during which one of the faculty explained its bafflingly simple mechanism, I learned more about the functioning of a jet engine and its component parts than I had gleaned during the several days I spent where they were in constant use. Many times while visiting the Academy of Aeronautics I thought of the good fortune of today's youth in having at its command such a wealth of facilities for equipping it to face life with the assurance that is born of practical knowledge.

Later when I sat with the vice president in his office and reviewed what I had seen and learned during my visit, I still had some questions I wanted answered.

"What is the background of the school faculty members?" I inquired.

"They hold many ratings as evidence of their ability," he replied. "College degrees, aircraft and aircraft engine mechanics' certificates, FAA instructor ratings, airplane pilot ratings, Federal Communications Commission's radio telephone operator third-class licenses. A most important qualification is their long years of industrial experience."

"How many hours are required for the complete course?"

"All Day Division courses are 2850 hours in length, or in terms of academic credits, 100 credit hours. Lecture hours represent 50% of the program and laboratory experience the other 50%. Graduates receive diplomas in their chosen areas of instruction. The graduate of the Aerospace Maintenance Technology course may apply to the Federal Aviation Agency for the Airframe and Powerplant Certificate. Many positions in aviation are closed to those who do not have this certificate. All graduates may apply for certification from the Institute for the Certification of Engineering Technicians."

"Why are FAA regulations so drastic?" I asked.

"You must remember," he answered, "that in aviation there is no middle ground between safety and risk. A commercial or private plane that deviates a hair's breadth from known safety standards in engineering or maintenance is grounded until it complies with FAA regulations. There is no such thing as a 'fairly safe' plane nor does the Federal Aviation Agency recognize pilots, engineers or maintenance technicians who fail to meet its standards. Where the safety of life and property is concerned, no regulations are too drastic, no standard of competence can be too high."

"And now," I questioned, "by what standards and controls are the schools themselves regulated?"

"They differ in degree and number in many of the states," he explained. "In New York state and in California for example, the regulations governing the operations of aeronautical schools are most exacting and properly so, since these states contain the major portion of the industry.

"Let's take the Academy of Aeronautics as an example. Its courses have been approved by the Federal Aviation Agency, the University of the State of New York, and the National Council of Technical Schools. The Engineers Council for Professional Development accredits all of these courses. Furthermore the final exams are conducted not by the school but by the FAA. Unless eighty per cent of the students taking the examination have passing marks, the school is ordered to discontinue by FAA. So you can see that to be properly accredited, an aeronautical school must prove that it can deliver to its students the training for which it has contracted."

During our lengthy discussion of the many phases of aviation, I was amazed at the depth and breadth of Lee Warrender's knowledge of the industry. The reporter's inquisitiveness prompted me to pry into his career.

A graduate of Massachusetts Institute of Technology, he served as a flier in World War I, and built up during the succeeding decades a nation-wide reputation as a skillful pilot, a mechanic of rare ability and as an aeronautical engineer with wide experience in the construction and maintenance of aircraft. For several years he directed the maintenance of the largest fleet of commercial aircraft in the United States. In the various activities in which he engaged, his watchword was "Thoroughness"; his philosophy, "If a job is worth doing, it is worth doing well."

While we chatted, planes continued to come in for landings every few minutes. Although their engines were throttled to a mere grumble, the spacious office vibrated with the spirit of aviation.

"Do you find that this location, so close to the activities of the airport, is a stimulus to your students?" I asked.

"Unquestionably," he said. "Students in any branch of

education are sensitive to environment, whether it be good or bad. A maritime school located on the desert many miles from water would be doomed to failure, no matter how good the instruction. Conversely, the many activities of an airport give ocular and aural evidence of aviation's need for competent men and women. More than six hundred planes enter and leave this airport every day. That means employment for about twelve thousand people. More than three million air passengers used LaGuardia Airport during the past year (and over eleven and one-half million the New York International Airport). Besides, over three million sight-seers, come each year to the airport to watch planes arrive and depart, bearing people of every nationality under the sun. If these facts and figures fail to arouse in the student a determination to make his mark in the aviation industry, he would be wise to look to other fields for his future livelihood."

"One more question," I interrupted. "What in your opinion does the future hold for aviation?"

"Only continued progress," he replied. "How far that progress shall reach, no living man can foretell. The most advanced aircraft of today will be obsolescent before their shiny newness has become tarnished. Jet rocket propulsion and nuclear power plants will soon be the general rule in commercial transport, entirely supplanting the internal combustion engine in use since the days of the Wright brothers. Electronic and hydraulic devices are already performing a multitude of tasks considered impossible a few years ago. New materials, new techniques, new appliances are introduced almost daily. The chief problem of the future will be the securing of well-trained personnel in sufficient numbers to cope with the ever-increasing complexities that will mark every branch of the industry."

My interview ended, I left for my home. As I drove along the parkway that skirts the airport for two miles, the giant hangars, the kaleidoscopic movement of people and planes, trucks and buses and motorcars took on a new significance. For here was an industry in full blast at which our fathers raised a questioning eyebrow but which has since changed the history of the world.

THE END